Integrated Language Arts Spelling Practice

Blackline Masters

Grade 6

D1211269

Copyright © 1996 Scholastic Inc. All rights reserved.   Published by Scholastic Inc.   Printed in the U.S.A.

ISBN 0-590-54539-6

1 2 3 4 5 6 7 8 9 10   33   03 02 01 00 99 98 97 96

CONTENTS

UNUSUAL SPELLINGS OF VOWEL SOUNDS

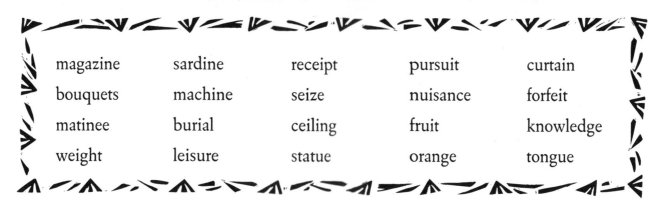

magazine	sardine	receipt	pursuit	curtain
bouquets	machine	seize	nuisance	forfeit
matinee	burial	ceiling	fruit	knowledge
weight	leisure	statue	orange	tongue

Choose words from the box that best complete the sentences below.

1. Jan ate an _____ while she read the _____ .

2. Al's antics were a _____ at the _____ performance.

3. He stuck his _____ out when the _____ came down.
   Then he tried to squeeze into my seat—I felt like a _____ !

4. Pat sent _____ of roses and baskets of _____ to his
   mother to celebrate her birthday.

5. The heavy _____ of the big copying _____ made her
   stagger. Then she lay down on the couch and stared at the _____ .

6. "The _____ of information is fine," Dad said. But he wasn't facing my
   homework and had enough _____ time to read his newspaper.

7. For more _____ about a subject, I consult an encyclopedia.

8. When the movers delivered the _____ to the museum, they asked
   for a _____ .

9. Because Teresa was sick, she had to _____ the last race. But after
   training hard, she plans to _____ the lead and win the next time.

10. After the _____ of Ian's pet frog, we all had a good cry.

With a partner, pick six words from the box and use them in a paragraph.
Read your paragraph to your partner and listen to his or hers. See how you
each used the same words differently.

SYNONYMS

desolate	pardon	fondness	hurried	unclear
deserted	excuse	abrupt	murky	costly
lonely	affection	hasty	gloomy	expensive
forgive	tenderness	rapid	obscure	high-priced

A. Each word below comes from the box above. Find synonyms in the box and write them next to each word.

1. deserted _____

2. excuse _____

3. fondness _____

4. hasty _____

5. gloomy _____

6. high-priced _____

B. Write words from the box that end with each suffix given below.

-ly	-y	-ed	-ness

Write a paragraph about an adventure.
Use at least four pairs of synonyms.

WORD BUILDING AND SOUND CHANGES

relative	application	declaration	priority	relate
compete	improvise	compositions	grammatical	historical
declare	competition	poetic	apply	prior
compose	history	improvisation	poetry	grammar

In each bubble below, write the related pairs of words from the list.

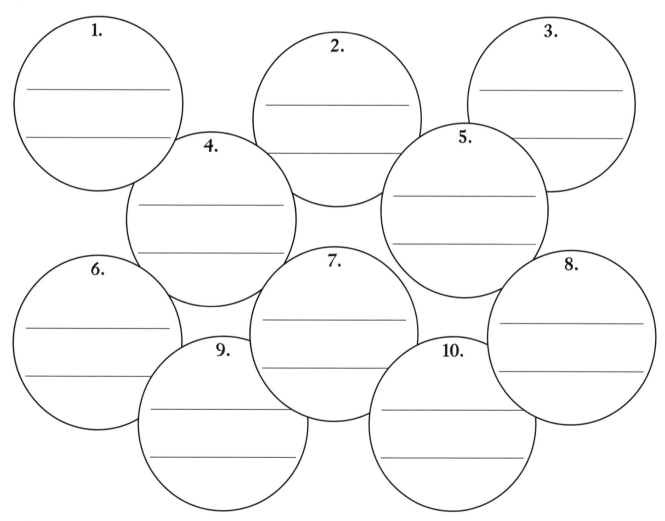

1.
2.
3.
4.
5.
6.
7.
8.
9.
10.

What other words do you know that come from base words? Use three of these words in sentences, and identify the base word. For example: I've always wanted to be a detective (detect).

SPELLING PATTERNS

heritage	all right	undertake	disown
image	toadstool	cheesecake	windblown
flashlight	car pool	snowflake	well-known
foresight	whirlpool	namesake	overgrown
spaceflight	footstool	rattlesnake	overthrown

Write a word from the box to complete each sentence. Then, in the blank below the sentence, write other words from the box with the same spelling pattern.

1. When we went trekking through the desert, I was scared silly of seeing a

   _____ .

   _____

2. I had a _____ in my backpack to frighten off animals in the night.

   _____

3. When we stopped for dinner my feet ached, and I wished I had a

   _____ to rest them on.

   _____

4. As we sat around the fire, a gusty breeze made our cheeks red and our hair

   _____ .

   _____

5. After that long walk, the _____ of my comfortable bed danced

   before my eyes.

   _____

With a partner, write a poem using words from the list that rhyme. Make it as silly or as serious as you like.

TECHNICAL WORDS

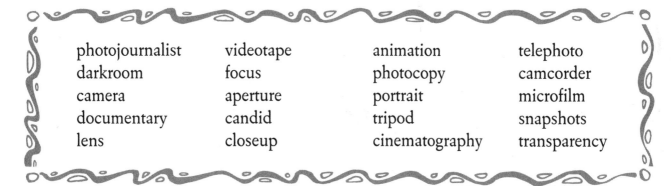

photojournalist	videotape	animation	telephoto
darkroom	focus	photocopy	camcorder
camera	aperture	portrait	microfilm
documentary	candid	tripod	snapshots
lens	closeup	cinematography	transparency

A. Choose the words from the box that best complete each sentence.

1. Christa used a _____ lens to photograph the nearby flower, and a _____ lens for the far-off bird. She needed a _____ to keep her camera steady.

2. They held the _____ up to the light to see it better.

3. The _____ went into the _____ to get the photos.

4. Have you seen the new _____ about migrant workers at the Rialto? It won an award for _____ .

5. Sylvester bought a _____ to use in his _____ to tape his sister's wedding.

B. Unscramble the letters below to form words from the box.

6. snel _____

7. yocthopop _____

8. arceam _____

9. clomifrim _____

10. rottpair _____

11. pantoshss _____

12. coufs _____

13. dinacd _____

14. tearpure _____

15. mainotain _____

 Imagine you're going to make a documentary film. Write a paragraph describing the equipment you'll need. Use as many words as you can from the spelling list.

SPELLING REVIEW

bouquets   desolate   competition   windblown   documentary

magazine   obscure   improvise   image   photojournalist

nuisance   expensive   application   well-known   videotape

knowledge   affection   historical   car pool   portrait

receipt   abrupt   poetry   all right   animation

How many syllables are in each word or word group from the box? Write the words on the chart.

2 syllables	3 syllables	4 syllables	5 syllables

Choose four words from the box and try to use them all in the same sentence. Compare your sentences with those of a partner.

Copyright © 1996 Scholastic Inc.

CONSONANTS /k/ AND /g/

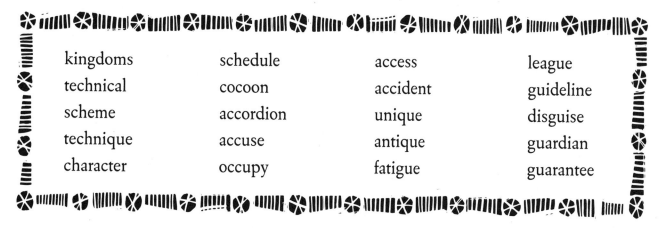

kingdoms	schedule	access	league
technical	cocoon	accident	guideline
scheme	accordion	unique	disguise
technique	accuse	antique	guardian
character	occupy	fatigue	guarantee

A. Combine the letters in the center of the wheel on the left with letters on the outer part to form six words from the box. Do the same with the wheel on the right to form three words from the box. You can use letters more than once.

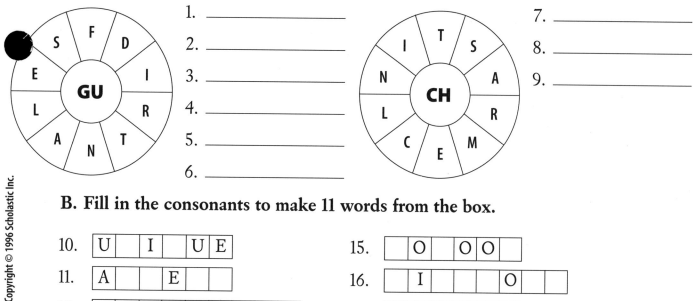

1. _____
2. _____
3. _____
4. _____
5. _____
6. _____

7. _____
8. _____
9. _____

B. Fill in the consonants to make 11 words from the box.

10. U _ I _ U E
11. A _ E _ _
12. A _ O _ I O _
13. _ _ E _ U _ E
14. A _ _ I _ U E

15. _ O _ O O _
16. _ I _ _ O _
17. _ E _ _ I _ U E
18. A _ _ U _ E
19. O _ _ U _ Y
20. A _ _ I _ E _ _

Write a list of at least three silly rules that will make people laugh. Use at least one word from the box in each rule. Can you use more than one?

ADDING SUFFIXES

equally	probable	ornamental	harmless
equal	emotional	ornament	harmful
definitely	emotion	merciful	harm
definite	coastal	merciless	faithful
probably	coast	mercy	faith

A. Fill in the chart with words from the box. In the first column, list each noun, the suffix added, and the adjective formed. In the second column, list each adjective, the suffix added, and the adverb formed.

Noun + Suffix = Adjective	Adjective + Suffix = Adverb

B. Which base words change their spelling before adding a suffix?

_____ changes *y* to *i*; _____ drops the *e*.

Write a short description of an interesting character (either real or imaginary). Use words from the box.

WORD BUILDING AND SOUND CHANGES

preparation	majesty	ritual	recognize
prepare	geographic	rite	analysis
miraculously	geography	triangulation	analyze
miracle	description	triangle	fabulous
majestic	describe	recognition	fable

A. Read each phonetic spelling below. Place an accent mark after the stressed syllable. Then write the word it represents.

1. (di skrīb) _____

2. (jē og rə fē) _____

3. (mə jes tik) _____

4. (mir ə kəl) _____

5. (pri pâr) _____

6. (rek əg nīz) _____

7. (di skrip shən) _____

8. (jē ə graf ik) _____

9. (maj ə stē) _____

10. (mi rak yə ləs) _____

11. (prep ə rā shən) _____

12. (rek əg nish ən) _____

B. Fill in each blank below with a word from the box.

13. A short tale used to teach a moral is a _____. Something in such a tale that is too wonderful to believe might be called _____.

14. A closed figure with three sides is a _____. A method for establishing the distance between any two points, based on that closed figure, is called _____.

15. A formal ceremony is a _____. An established way of performing a ceremony is a _____.

16. To examine carefully is to _____. The process of examining or investigating is called an _____.

GEOGRAPHIC WORDS

Iditarod	Arctic	Ptarmigan	icebound
Nome	Bering Sea	caribou	snowshoes
Anchorage	Yukon River	parka	headlamp
Aleutian Islands	Juneau	blizzard	towline
Alaska	moose	igloo	mukluks

A. List as many words from the box as you can that fit each category below.

1. States: _____

2. Cities or towns: _____

3. Bodies of water: _____

4. Islands: _____

5. Animals: _____

6. Articles of clothing: _____

B. Read the clues below. Then complete the puzzle with words from the box.

ACROSS

7. a severe snowstorm

10. a rope for pulling something

11. a traditional Alaskan dwelling

12. a light worn on a hat or cap

DOWN

8. held fast or shut off by ice

9. at or near the North Pole

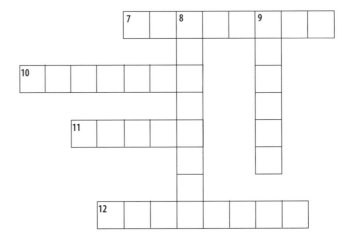

 Write a travel ad for a trip to Alaska. Use as many words from the box as you can.

INVENTED WORDS

nylon	linoleum	trampoline	windbreaker
tarmac	minibike	escalator	spoof
dynamite	yo-yo	thermos	blurb
aspirin	zippered	tabloid	boondoggle
cellophane	kerosene	aluminum	scrooge

A. From the box above, list the words that go under each of the categories below.

1. Play and Entertainment **2. Unpleasant Things** **3. Materials**

_____ _____ _____

_____ _____ _____

_____ _____ _____

_____

B. Choose words from the box that best complete the sentences below.

4. Rico put on his _____ and _____ it up tight. It would be cold at the airport _____.

5. He was carrying a _____ of coffee and some roses wrapped in _____ as he went to meet Rosa's plane.

6. The headlines in the _____ on the newsstand caught his attention— "Police Say Sticks of _____ Caused Airport Explosion."

7. Someone had also poured _____ onto an abandoned building.

8. He took an _____ to stop his throbbing headache and jumped onto the _____ headed for the mezzanine.

9. He bought a book whose jacket _____ sounded exciting.

SPELLING REVIEW

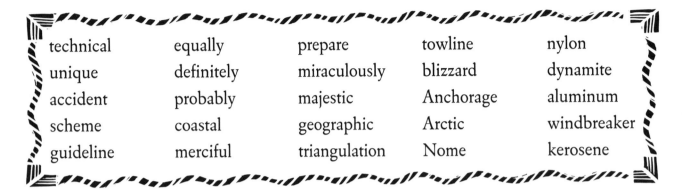

technical	equally	prepare	towline	nylon
unique	definitely	miraculously	blizzard	dynamite
accident	probably	majestic	Anchorage	aluminum
scheme	coastal	geographic	Arctic	windbreaker
guideline	merciful	triangulation	Nome	kerosene

A. Write words from the box that come between each pair of dictionary guide words.

1. accept/ardent	2. noisy/process	3. tea/unit

4. mend/miss	5. deed/dynasty	6. gem/gum

B. Fill in the missing letters to make seven words from the box.

 Create a crossword puzzle. Choose at least six words from the box. Don't forget the clues!

THE SCHWA SOUND

beggar	liar	sponsor	visitor	factual
flavor	scholar	editor	sculptor	Capitol
collar	cellar	manager	mirror	capital
peddler	pillar	senator	actual	customer

A. List the "one who" word that matches each activity.

1. A _____ peddles.

2. A _____ sculpts.

3. A _____ goes to school.

4. A _____ begs.

5. A _____ visits.

6. A _____ supports something.

7. A _____ lies.

8. A _____ manages.

9. A _____ makes laws.

10. An _____ edits.

11. A _____ buys things.

B. Write sentences using the remaining words that are nouns or adjectives.

_____

_____

_____

_____

_____

_____

_____

_____

SUFFIXES: -AGE, -SHIP, -EN, -TION, -ER

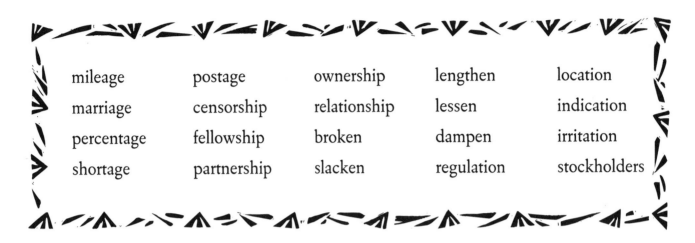

mileage	postage	ownership	lengthen	location
marriage	censorship	relationship	lessen	indication
percentage	fellowship	broken	dampen	irritation
shortage	partnership	slacken	regulation	stockholders

Fill in the chart with words from the box.

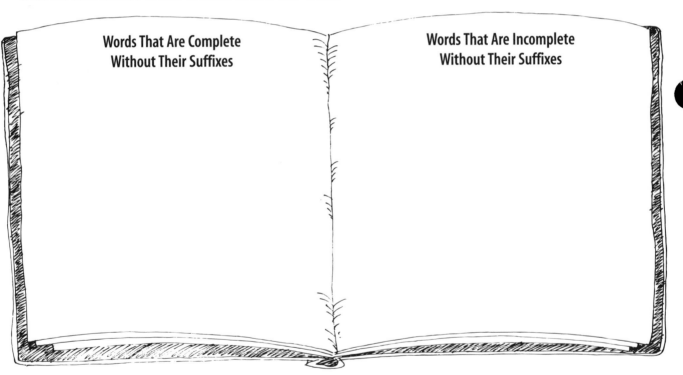

Words That Are Complete Without Their Suffixes

Words That Are Incomplete Without Their Suffixes

What is the only word that is neither a noun nor a verb?

Word: _____   Part of speech: _____

Write four sentences about your day at school. Use at least one word from the box in each sentence.

STRESS SHIFT

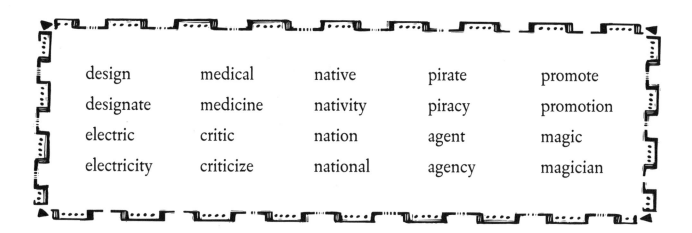

design	medical	native	pirate	promote
designate	medicine	nativity	piracy	promotion
electric	critic	nation	agent	magic
electricity	criticize	national	agency	magician

Complete the chart below using words from the box. Read the words and listen for changes in vowel sounds. Underline the syllables that are stressed in each pair.

Base Word	Base Word + Suffix
Example: *register*	Example: *registration*

Use words from the box to write a review of a song you've heard on the radio.

HOMOGRAPHS

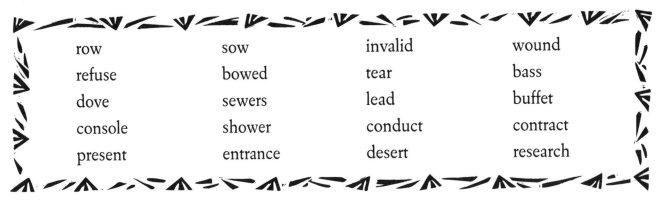

row	sow	invalid	wound
refuse	bowed	tear	bass
dove	sewers	lead	buffet
console	shower	conduct	contract
present	entrance	desert	research

List the words in the box in the correct columns. Most words can go in two columns. Saying the words aloud and noticing the different ways they can be pronounced can help you identify how the words are used.

Nouns	Verbs	Adjectives

Use words from the box or other homographs you can think of to write a silly poem.

BLENDED AND SHORTENED WORDS

flurry	squiggle	bionic	slosh	broasted
smog	motel	glimmer	sprig	movie
splatter	twirl	flush	telecast	dumbfound
brunch	splotch	smash	co-op	bike

Complete the equations with a blended word from the box.

glisten + shimmer = _____

smoke + fog = _____

television + broadcast = _____

broiled + roasted = _____

flutter + hurry = _____

splash + spatter = _____

biology + electronics = _____

moving + picture = _____

dumb + confound = _____

breakfast + lunch = _____

twist + whirl = _____

motor + hotel = _____

squirm + wiggle = _____

spot + blotch = _____

spray + twig = _____

flash + gush = _____

slop + slush = _____

smack + mash = _____

The words that are left are shortened forms of longer words. Write them below.

_____

_____

 Make up some funny word blends. List the words and write their definitions.

SPELLING REVIEW

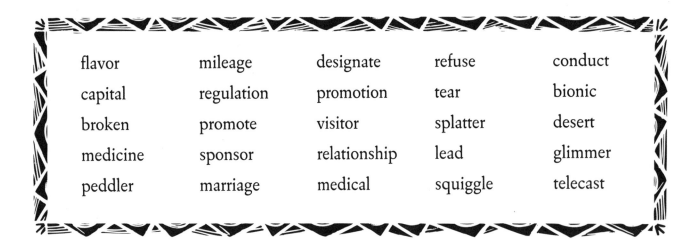

flavor	mileage	designate	refuse	conduct
capital	regulation	promotion	tear	bionic
broken	promote	visitor	splatter	desert
medicine	sponsor	relationship	lead	glimmer
peddler	marriage	medical	squiggle	telecast

Decide how many syllables are in each word from the box. Write the words on the chart, then draw lines between the syllables.

1-syllable words	2-syllable words	3-syllable words	4-syllable words

Write "What Am I?" riddles for seven words from the box. For example, "I am the taste of something, like chocolate or vanilla. What am I?" *(flavor)* See if a friend can guess the answers to your riddles.

WORDS WITH /CH/, /SH/, /ZH/

exchanging	snatching	ancient	challenge
establish	conditions	appreciate	sugar
ferocious	measure	crucial	erosion
vision	casual	concerto	equation
decision	century	exhaustion	chariot

A. Write the words in the box that have the /sh/ sound.
Circle the letters that make the sound.

B. Write the words in the box that have the /zh/ sound.
Circle the letters that make the sound.

C. Write the words in the box that have the /ch/ sound.
Circle the letters that make the sound.

Make a list of more words that end in -*tion*. Then order them under the headings /zh/ or /sh/.

BASE: *PRESS, PUT, CAP, TEST*

suppressed	protest	capsule	impression
dispute	computation	contest	repute
express	captive	reputation	captured
capable	depression	compute	capacity
testify	deputy	compress	detest

Write the spelling word that matches each meaning below.

Words with *press*

1. sadness _____

2. say or show _____

3. put an end to _____

4. force into less space _____

5. a deep effect _____

Words with *cap*

6. a prisoner _____

7. taken prisoner _____

8. the most _____

9. case or container _____

10. able _____

Fill in each box with words that contain the base word written on top.

Words with *test*
_____
_____
_____
_____

Words with *put*
_____
_____
_____
_____
_____

Write a sentence that uses a word from each of the four word bases.

BASES AND ROOTS: *NAT, VIS, TRACT, POS*

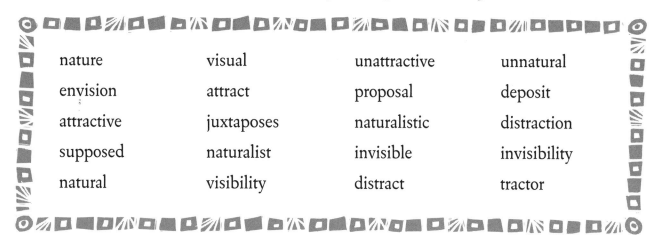

nature	visual	unattractive	unnatural
envision	attract	proposal	deposit
attractive	juxtaposes	naturalistic	distraction
supposed	naturalist	invisible	invisibility
natural	visibility	distract	tractor

A. Find the six words in the box that have the root *tract*. Write which are verbs, which are nouns, and which are adjectives. You may use a dictionary to help you.

Nouns	Adjectives	Verbs
_____	_____	_____
_____	_____	_____

B. Write a word from the box that best completes each sentence. Then on the line underneath, write all the other words from the box that use the same base or root.

1. When I grow up, I want to be a _____ .

_____

2. I _____ a wonderful future.

_____

3. I have found out what you are _____ to study to enter this profession.

_____

Pick one of the bases or roots and find all the words in the box that use it. Write a different sentence that uses each word.

WORD HISTORIES

fangs	monster	apron	debris
orange	silhouetted	quiz	planet
bonfire	cyclone	galaxy	tentacles
neighbor	asteroid	tote	salary
muscle	umpire	geranium	alarm

Complete the analogy with a word from the box.

1. flower : daisy
   as color: _____

2. swim : bathing suit
   as cook: _____

3. Lassie : dog
   as Frankenstein: _____

4. fruit : apple
   as flower: _____

5. United States : country
   as Mars: _____

6. movie : director
   as baseball: _____

7. world : continent
   as universe: _____

8. wisdom : brain
   as strength: _____

9. practice : game
   as study: _____

10. throw : toss
    as carry: _____

11. switch : light bulb
    as match: _____

12. humans : legs
    as squid: _____

13. school : education
    as job: _____

14. asleep : lullaby
    as awake: _____

15. soft : pillows
    as sharp: _____

16. school : classmate
    as street: _____

17. three-dimensional : sculptured
    as two-dimensional: _____

18. ocean : fish
    as outer space: _____

19. vacuum : dust
    as sweep: _____

20. water : whirlpool
    as wind: _____

WORD PAIRS

stationary	affect	principal	forward
stationery	effects	principle	foreword
immigrate	envelop	proceed	
emigrate	envelope	precede	
accept	farther	collage	
except	further	college	

A. Match words from the box with the clues below.

1. a school _____

2. ahead _____

3. standing still _____

4. moral belief _____

5. influence or change _____

6. continue _____

7. come to a new country _____

8. go in front of _____

9. beginning of a book _____

10. writing paper _____

11. leader of a school _____

12. results _____

13. leave a country _____

14. work of art _____

B. Complete each sentence by filling the blanks with a word from the box.

15. I _____ the gift you sent me

16. _____, I thank you for your generosity.

17. The scarves _____ me like a cape.

18. I've worn them every day _____ Thursday.

19. The thank-you card in the yellow _____ just went into the mail.

20. I don't have to walk any _____ than the post office.

Choose three pairs of words from the box. Write a sentence for each word.

SPELLING REVIEW

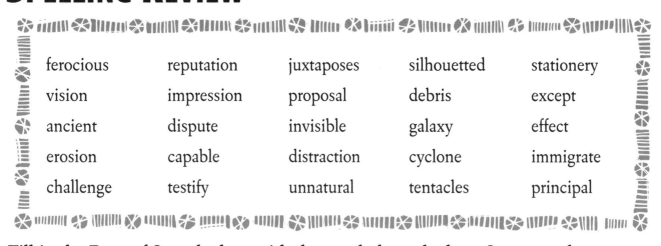

ferocious	reputation	juxtaposes	silhouetted	stationery
vision	impression	proposal	debris	except
ancient	dispute	invisible	galaxy	effect
erosion	capable	distraction	cyclone	immigrate
challenge	testify	unnatural	tentacles	principal

Fill in the Parts of Speech chart with the words from the box. Some words may be two parts of speech. Write them on both parts of the chart.

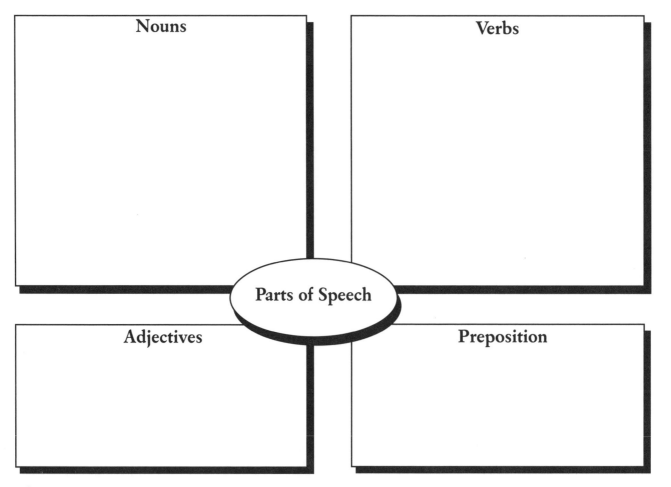

Nouns

Verbs

Parts of Speech

Adjectives

Preposition

Write a radio or movie script. Use at least seven words from the box.

WORDS WITH /är/ AND /ôr/

gorgeous	enormous	endorse	parcel
compartments	organize	platform	dormitory
starboard	hearth	corporation	harvest
startled	cornstarch	radar	department
partial	boulevard	assortment	starvation

A. Unscramble the words in each box below to form a word from the box above. Then underline the letters that spell /är/ or /ôr/.

/är/	/ôr/
1. tharhe: _____	**13.** soremuno: _____
2. drovuable: _____	**14.** zenigaro: _____
3. adarr: _____	**15.** shaccnorrt: _____
4. thavers: _____	**16.** dresone: _____
5. sledratt: _____	**17.** floptram: _____
6. troavstain: _____	**18.** rootcapniro: _____
7. sprontammect: _____	**19.** stranomets: _____
8. martpented: _____	**20.** yordmitor: _____
9. platira: _____	**21.** rougesgo: _____
10. schrocrant: _____	
11. claper: _____	
12. bradtoras: _____	

B. **22.** Which word has both /är/ and /ôr/ sounds? _____

23. Which word has two /ôr/ sounds? _____

24. Which word has an unusual spelling for /är/? _____

ROOTS: *JECT, GRAV, SPHER, SPIR*

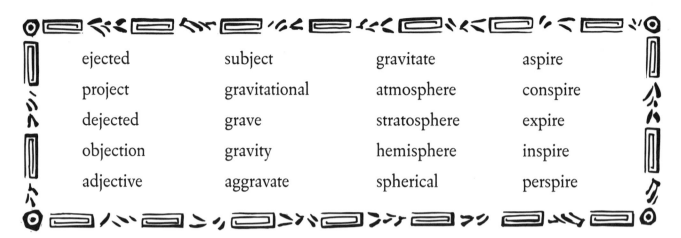

ejected	subject	gravitate	aspire
project	gravitational	atmosphere	conspire
dejected	grave	stratosphere	expire
objection	gravity	hemisphere	inspire
adjective	aggravate	spherical	perspire

A. Match each clue with a word from the box. Underline the root.

1. sweat: _____

2. round in shape: _____

3. serious: _____

4. aim for: _____

5. make worse: _____

6. half of the globe: _____

7. depressed: _____

8. long-term assignment: _____

9. plot together: _____

10. describing word: _____

11. thrown out: _____

12. heaviness or weight: _____

13. be strongly attracted: _____

14. come to an end: _____

B. Complete the puzzle with other words from the box.

15. [ ][ ][ ][ ][ ][ ][S][ ][ ][ ][ ]

16. [P]

17. [ ][ ][ ][ ][ ][H][ ][ ]

18. [ ][E][ ]

19. [R][ ][ ][ ][ ][ ][ ][ ][ ][ ]

20. [ ][ ][ ][E][ ][ ][ ]

Choose two roots above, and draw two family trees. Make each root the trunk of one tree. Then think of as many words as you can with that root and write them on the branches.

ROOTS: *VERT/VERS, MIT/MISS, SPOND*

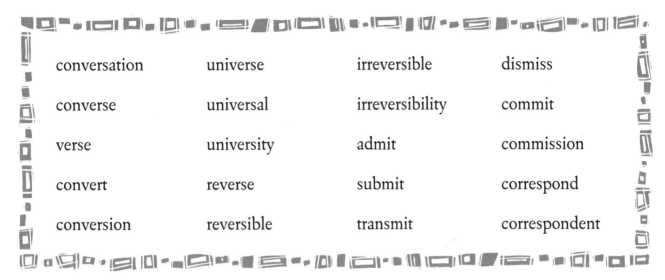

conversation	universe	irreversible	dismiss
converse	universal	irreversibility	commit
verse	university	admit	commission
convert	reverse	submit	correspond
conversion	reversible	transmit	correspondent

The words in the box are nouns, verbs, and adjectives. Write them on the chart under the correct heading. Some words can be used more than once. Use a dictionary to help you.

Noun	Verb	Adjective

Pick three words from the box whose meanings you don't know. Look in a dictionary for their definitions. Then use the words in sentences.

WORDS FROM LANGUAGES OTHER THAN ENGLISH

bagel	spinach	pajamas	tundra
clown	bandit	yam	gorilla
chocolate	karate	coffee	jubilee
landscape	bamboo	hammock	outrage
ketchup	ukulele	kangaroo	investigation

A. Write the word from the box that completes each analogy.

1. orange: carrot as green: _____

2. opera: singer as circus: _____

3. slither: snake as hop: _____

4. architect: building as gardener: _____

5. cake: angel food as bread: _____

6. leaf: tea as bean: _____

7. jam: fruit as candy: _____

8. shoe: slipper as suit: _____

9. tree: oak as grass: _____

10. sit: chair as lie: _____

B. Write the word from the box that belongs in each group.

11. inquiry, examination, _____

12. guitar, banjo, _____

13. chimpanzee, orangutan, _____

14. desert, prairie, _____

15. robber, outlaw, _____

16. shock, offend, _____

17. judo, tae kwon do, _____

18. celebration, festivity, _____

19. mustard, relish, _____

20. potato, sweet potato, _____

Pick three words from the box. Find out more about the histories of these words in a dictionary or other source. Share what you learn.

WORDS WITH RELATED MEANINGS

enchantment	disturb	journey	terror
appeal	messenger	trek	dread
panic	carrier	cruise	demand
hysteria	necessary	voyage	command
intrude	vital	horror	order

Answer each question below with words from the box.

1. Which four words mean "great fear"?_____

2. Which of the words you just wrote can refer to fear so great that it produces an anxiety disorder? _____ Which other word means "an emotional disorder or uncontrollable outburst"? _____

3. Which four words mean "a trip"?_____

4. Which three words refer to asking someone to do something?_____
Which two words would you use to refer to an officer speaking to troops?_____
_____

5. Which two words mean "to bother someone"?_____Which word means "to come in without permission"?_____

6. Which two words refer to something that is very important or essential? _____
_____Which word specifically means "essential to life"?_____

7. Which two words mean "the power to attract"?_____Which word might include a magical influence?_____

8. Which two words involve a person bringing or transporting something from one place to another?_____

Write a paragraph describing a TV or movie adventure you've seen or would like to see. Use as many words from the box as you can.

SPELLING REVIEW

enormous	aggravate	universal	landscape	enchantment
assortment	atmosphere	university	chocolate	panic
endorse	gravitational	reversible	outrage	disturb
gorgeous	objection	correspondent	ketchup	hysteria
parcel	perspire	commit	investigation	messenger

A. Match words from the box with the clues below.

1. interrupt _____

2. entrust _____

3. approve _____

4. air _____

5. package _____

6. argument against _____

7. mixture _____

8. huge _____

9. college _____

10. beautiful _____

11. involving all _____

12. reporter _____

B. Suppose A = 1, B = 2, C = 3, and so on. Write the word from the box for each number code below.

13. 3-8-15-3-15-12-1-20-5 _____

14. 13-5-19-19-5-14-7-5-18 _____

15. 1-7-7-18-1-22-1-20-5 _____

16. 16-1-14-9-3 _____

17. 11-5-20-3-8-21-16 _____

18. 15-21-20-18-1-7-5 _____

19. 8-25-19-20-5-18-9-1 _____

20. 5-14-3-8-1-14-20-13-5-14-20 _____

21. 7-18-1-22-9-20-1-20-9-15-14-1-12 _____

22. 12-1-14-4-19-3-1-16-5 _____

23. 18-5-22-5-18-19-9-2-12-5 _____

24. 9-14-22-5-19-20-9-7-1-20-9-15-14 _____

25. 16-5-18-19-16-9-18-5 _____

UNSTRESSED SYLLABLES

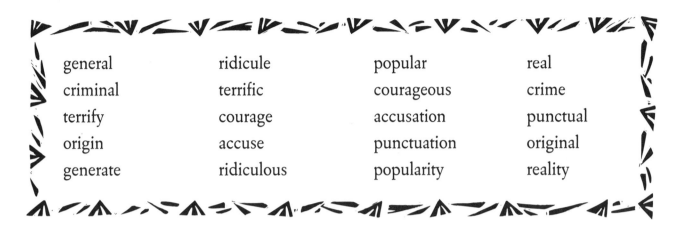

general	ridicule	popular	real
criminal	terrific	courageous	crime
terrify	courage	accusation	punctual
origin	accuse	punctuation	original
generate	ridiculous	popularity	reality

A. For each pair of words listed below, indicate the change in the stressed syllable. Divide each word into syllables and mark with an accent (') the syllable that is stressed. Use a dictionary to help you.

1. popular _____

   popularity _____

2. ridiculous _____

   ridicule _____

3. accuse _____

   accusation _____

4. punctuation _____

   punctual _____

5. origin _____

   original _____

6. courageous _____

   courage _____

B. On the lines below, give the information asked for.

7. Two pairs of words from the box have the same number of syllables. Name the pairs and write the number of syllables.

   _____

8. In two pairs of words, one word has only one syllable. Name the pairs.

   _____

 From the list, choose a word with three syllables, four syllables, and five syllables. Write a sentence using each word.

DOUBLE CONSONANTS

suggest	assumed	effort	immense
appearance	immature	irregular	assignment
illegal	appetite	account	annex
collaborate	affairs	commotion	suppress
occupied	committee	sufficient	attorneys

Place the words from the box in the correct list. Some words may fit in more than one list.

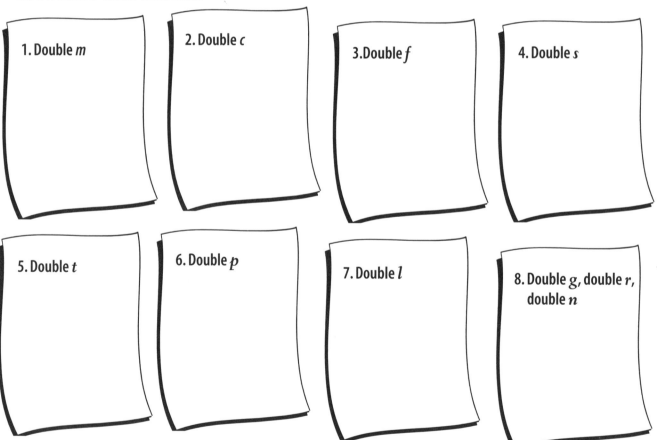

1. Double *m*

2. Double *c*

3. Double *f*

4. Double *s*

5. Double *t*

6. Double *p*

7. Double *l*

8. Double *g*, double *r*, double *n*

Write a brief newspaper article about something that happened in your school recently. Use at least five words from the box.

GREEK ROOTS AND COMBINING FORMS

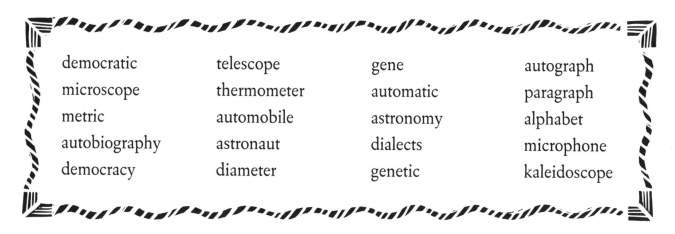

democratic	telescope	gene	autograph
microscope	thermometer	automatic	paragraph
metric	automobile	astronomy	alphabet
autobiography	astronaut	dialects	microphone
democracy	diameter	genetic	kaleidoscope

A. Provide answers to each item with words from the box.

1. Words that begin with the Greek word for *star*

_____

2. Words that begin with the Greek word for *self*

_____

3. Words that contain the Greek word for *measure*

_____

4. Words that contain the Greek word for *look at*

_____

5. Words that contain the Greek word for *people*

_____

B. Match words from the box with these clues.

6. Unit of heredity _____

7. Forms of a language _____

8. Related to origins _____

9. Letters _____

10. Loudspeaker _____

11. Group of sentences _____

SPELLING ACROSS THE CURRICULUM

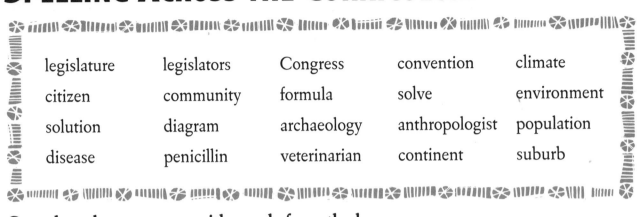

legislature	legislators	Congress	convention	climate
citizen	community	formula	solve	environment
solution	diagram	archaeology	anthropologist	population
disease	penicillin	veterinarian	continent	suburb

Complete the sentences with words from the box.

1. A _____ is an animal doctor.

2. _____ is a medicine used to fight _____.
   A chemist knows the _____ for preparing this medicine.

3. The U.S. Senate and House of Representatives make up the _____.
   Within states, lawmakers—or _____—meet in the
   _____.

4. Scientists who study _____ learn about ancient peoples. A(n)
   _____ examines the customs and beliefs of societies today.

5. The weather, or _____, and other conditions on a
   _____ can affect the _____.

6. In a _____, a _____ may meet with other
   residents at a _____ to discuss neighborhood concerns.

7. To _____ the problem, the mathematicians drew a
   _____. It helped them find the _____.

8. The _____ of a _____ is usually smaller
   than that of a city.

Choose one subject area suggested by the list of words (government, medicine, science). Using as many words as you can from the list, write a news story from your imagination.

OLD SPELLINGS TO NEW

tomorrow	rhyme	debt	perfect	foreign
straight	money	acre	doubt	school
island	aisle	stomach	scissors	surprise
soldier	limb	ghost	bridge	warden

A. Some of the words from the box contain silent consonants. The consonants are printed here. Fill in the rest of the word.

1. _ _ _ _ _ _ g h _

2. _ _ s _ _ _

3. _ h _ _ _ _

4. _ _ _ _ _ _ g _

5. _ s _ _ _ _

6. _ _ _ b

7. _ _ b _

8. _ _ _ b _

9. _ h _ _ _

10. _ c _ _ _ _ _ _

B. Read the clues. Then complete the puzzle with words from the box.

ACROSS

2. the next day
5. a piece of land
6. unexpected event
7. warrior
8. place for learning

DOWN

1. a structure across water
3. coins and bills
4. a guard
6. a part of the body
9. without error

SPELLING REVIEW

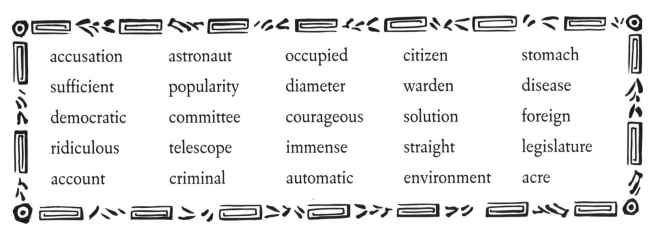

accusation	astronaut	occupied	citizen	stomach
sufficient	popularity	diameter	warden	disease
democratic	committee	courageous	solution	foreign
ridiculous	telescope	immense	straight	legislature
account	criminal	automatic	environment	acre

Write the words from the box in alphabetical order in the correct column below.

A–C

D–J

K–Z

Create a crossword puzzle. Choose at least six words from the box. Put the clues in an Across list and a Down list.

magazine	ceiling
bouquets	statue
matinee	pursuit
weight	nuisance
sardine	fruit
machine	orange
burial	curtain
leisure	forfeit
receipt	knowledge
seize	tongue

1. Have you seen the latest issue of my wildlife **magazine**?
2. The singer received several **bouquets** of flowers.
3. The movie **matinee** starts at 2:30 on Saturday.
4. Because of its **weight**, the package needed a lot of postage.
5. Henry ate a **sardine** and tomato sandwich for lunch.
6. The tailor stitched up the hem on his sewing **machine**.
7. My little sister held a short **burial** service for her pet worm.
8. Uncle Mike spends all his **leisure** time playing golf.
9. The **receipt** says that the package was delivered on April 19.
10. Let's **seize** that thief before he gets away!
11. Magda decided to paint the **ceiling** of her room sky blue.
12. That **statue** was carved from one piece of marble.
13. The car sped away with several police cars in **pursuit**.
14. Ants at a picnic can really be a **nuisance**.
15. The Goldbergs sent us a basket of **fruit** from Florida.
16. The sun appeared **orange** in the hazy sky.
17. As the **curtain** came down, the audience booed and whistled.
18. The hockey player had to **forfeit** a day's pay for fighting.
19. Dr. Greco's **knowledge** of astronomy is quite remarkable.
20. The doctor told the patient to stick out her **tongue**.

desolate	hasty
deserted	rapid
lonely	hurried
forgive	murky
pardon	gloomy
excuse	obscure
affection	unclear
tenderness	costly
fondness	expensive
abrupt	high-priced

1. The treeless landscape seemed **desolate**.
2. The survivors of the shipwreck landed on a **deserted** island.
3. After Joanna left for college, her younger sister felt **lonely**.
4. Please **forgive** me for forgetting our appointment.
5. Mickey begged Minnie's **pardon** for stepping on her toe.
6. The gym teacher will **excuse** you just this once.
7. Mrs. Grant shows her **affection** by pampering her poodle.
8. Father showed **tenderness** as he comforted the weeping child.
9. Stan's **fondness** for fishing is well-known.
10. His **abrupt** departure upset the whole family.
11. The outnumbered soldiers made a **hasty** retreat.
12. The detective fired a **rapid** series of questions at the suspect.
13. She **hurried** to answer the ringing telephone.
14. The fog and rain made the day **murky**.
15. The **gloomy** old house sat forlornly on the hill.
16. The new president comes from an **obscure** village in the north.
17. Your paragraph is poorly written, and its meaning is **unclear**.
18. That mistake will be very **costly** for the company.
19. Marie was upset after losing the **expensive** bracelet.
20. We cannot afford that **high-priced** car.

competition	improvise
compete	improvisation
compositions	grammar
compose	grammatical
poetry	apply
poetic	application
relative	history
relate	historical
declaration	prior
declare	priority

1. The freestyle swimming **competition** will begin in five minutes.
2. Will Yoko **compete** in the marathon race this year?
3. Our teacher has just finished marking all our **compositions**.
4. You can use your research notes to **compose** your speech.
5. Have you ever tried writing **poetry** that doesn't rhyme?
6. That line about washing your bike doesn't seem very **poetic**.
7. Cousin Leroy is our only **relative** who lives in town.
8. Gina can **relate** the story of how we got lost better than I can.
9. The governor made a **declaration** that tomorrow will be a state holiday.
10. The customs agent asked if we had anything to **declare**.
11. Since we don't know the words to the song, we will **improvise**.
12. That theater company is very good at **improvisation**.
13. We had a **grammar** lesson on irregular verbs.
14. Be sure your business letter is neat, clear, and **grammatical**.
15. Did Wilson **apply** for the after-school job at the diner?
16. He filled out the job **application** form yesterday.
17. That **history** book is so dated that it ends in 1975.
18. It is a **historical** fact that most American women couldn't vote until 1920.
19. The Molinas stopped at the florist **prior** to going to the party.
20. Cleaning the basement has top **priority** at our house today.

heritage	undertake
image	cheesecake
flashlight	snowflake
foresight	namesake
spaceflight	rattlesnake
all right	disown
toadstool	windblown
car pool	well-known
whirlpool	overgrown
footstool	overthrown

1. Latisha is proud of her African-American **heritage**.
2. His **image** stared back at him from the mirror.
3. We turned on the **flashlight** as we approached the dark alley.
4. Abe had the **foresight** to do his homework early last night.
5. The **spaceflight** of *Apollo 13* was a nerve-racking experience.
6. It's **all right** to leave your muddy boots in the hallway.
7. A **toadstool** is a poisonous mushroom.
8. Four parents are part of an after-school **car pool**.
9. The paddlers carefully avoided the **whirlpool** in the river.
10. Aunt Barbara rested her broken ankle on a **footstool**.
11. My brother and I will **undertake** the task of cleaning our room Saturday.
12. We all enjoyed the **cheesecake** that Uncle Charlie baked.
13. Is it possible that every **snowflake** that falls is different?
14. Mathilda is the **namesake** of her Grandma Tillie.
15. A **rattlesnake** actually has a rattle at the end of its tail.
16. The rich woman decided to **disown** her absent son.
17. Let me comb my **windblown** hair.
18. Tim's dad is a **well-known** columnist.
19. That **overgrown** yard could certainly use a gardener.
20. After his government was **overthrown**, the dictator fled to a Pacific island.

photojournalist	animation
darkroom	photocopy
camera	portrait
documentary	tripod
lens	cinematography
videotape	telephoto
focus	camcorder
aperture	microfilm
candid	snapshots
closeup	transparency

1. Nan's sister is a **photojournalist** for a national newsmagazine.
2. She has a **darkroom** in her apartment, where she develops her photos.
3. I bought a roll of film to try out my new **camera**.
4. Did you see the **documentary** about South Africa on TV last night?
5. Mr. Franklin bought a wide-angle **lens** for his camera.
6. We can **videotape** the special program so we won't miss it.
7. The new baby was the **focus** of everyone's attention.
8. This photo is too dark because the **aperture** was too small.
9. He was very **candid** about his experiences as a prisoner of war.
10. The **closeup** of the dagger made the audience gasp.
11. Her lack of **animation** was caused by a sleepless night.
12. Make a **photocopy** of the letter in case it gets lost.
13. Lady Alicia's **portrait** hangs over the mantel.
14. He placed his camera on a **tripod** to keep it steady.
15. Leon will study **cinematography** in film school.
16. You'll need a **telephoto** lens to get the best photos of wild animals.
17. Grandma used her **camcorder** at the birthday party.
18. The spy slipped the **microfilm** of the secret plans into her earring.
19. Those **snapshots** of the family picnic are really funny.
20. He held the **transparency** up to the light so we could all see it.

bouquets	historical
magazine	poetry
nuisance	windblown
knowledge	image
receipt	well-known
desolate	car pool
obscure	all right
expensive	documentary
affection	photojournalist
abrupt	videotape
competition	portrait
improvise	animation
application	

1. The singer received several **bouquets** of flowers.
2. Have you seen the latest issue of my wildlife **magazine**?
3. Ants at a picnic can really be a **nuisance**.
4. Dr. Greco's **knowledge** of astronomy is quite remarkable.
5. The **receipt** says that the package was delivered on April 19.
6. The treeless landscape seemed **desolate**.
7. The new president comes from an **obscure** village in the north.
8. Marie was upset after losing the **expensive** bracelet.
9. Mrs. Grant shows her **affection** by pampering her poodle.
10. His **abrupt** departure upset the whole family.
11. The freestyle swimming **competition** will begin in five minutes.
12. Since we don't know the words to the song, we will **improvise**.
13. He filled out the job **application** form yesterday.
14. It is a **historical** fact that most American women couldn't vote until 1920.
15. Have you ever tried writing **poetry** that doesn't rhyme?
16. Let me comb my **windblown** hair.
17. His **image** stared back at him from the mirror.
18. Tim's dad is a **well-known** columnist.
19. Four parents are part of an after-school **car pool**.
20. It's **all right** to leave your muddy boots in the hallway.
21. Did you see the **documentary** about South Africa on TV last night?
22. Nan's sister is a **photojournalist** for a national newsmagazine.
23. We can **videotape** the special program so we won't miss it.
24. Lady Alicia's **portrait** hangs over the mantel.
25. Her lack of **animation** was caused by a sleepless night.

kingdoms	occupy
fatigue	character
technical	unique
accordion	access
cocoon	accident
league	disguise
guideline	guardian
scheme	guarantee
technique	antique
accuse	schedule

1. The queen toured the two **kingdoms** with her husband.
2. All this work may **fatigue** you.
3. This computer book is highly **technical**.
4. The **accordion** is one of my favorite musical instruments.
5. Which insect builds a **cocoon**?
6. The two soccer teams joined the county's soccer **league**.
7. The **guideline** gives us helpful information.
8. Will this **scheme** for building a model airplane really work?
9. Learning to play the violin requires practicing one's **technique**.
10. What did they **accuse** that person of doing?
11. Three offices and a store **occupy** that building.
12. Who is the most interesting **character** in that story?
13. Carlos's visit to the Grand Canyon was a **unique** experience.
14. Which door provides **access** to the building?
15. He wasn't seriously hurt in the automobile **accident**.
16. Children love to **disguise** themselves on Halloween.
17. While the child's parents were away, Ms. Cho was the **guardian**.
18. The **guarantee** allowed us to return the broken television.
19. This **antique** might be over one hundred years old.
20. Our **schedule** includes an appointment at three o'clock.

equally	merciful
equal	merciless
definitely	mercy
definite	ornamental
probably	ornament
probable	harmless
emotional	harmful
emotion	harm
coastal	faithful
coast	faith

1. The rules apply **equally** to both teams in the game.
2. One pint is **equal** to 16 ounces.
3. He **definitely** promised to finish the work today.
4. The arrangement is **definite** and cannot be changed.
5. Jan will **probably** visit us today, but his plans are not final.
6. Bad weather was the **probable** reason for the delay.
7. Your **emotional** response to the bad news is understandable.
8. Happiness is an example of a common human **emotion**.
9. The boat neared the island's **coastal** waters.
10. We spotted a porpoise off the **coast** of Florida.
11. The lawyer begged the judge to be **merciful** to the prisoner.
12. **Merciless** winners show cruelty to their defeated enemies.
13. The kind police officer treated the young people with **mercy**.
14. Wanda's kitchen was decorated with **ornamental** plants.
15. Please hang this **ornament** over the fireplace.
16. That **harmless** dog certainly wouldn't bite you.
17. If taken in large amounts, that medicine can be **harmful**.
18. I'm sure the playful child didn't mean to do any **harm**.
19. The **faithful** employee never missed a day of work.
20. We have **faith** in your ability to do well on the project.

PLAN III

prepare	ritual
● preparation	rite
miraculously	triangulation
miracle	triangle
majesty	recognize
majestic	recognition
geographic	analyze
geography	analysis
describe	fable
description	fabulous

PLAN III

1. We should **prepare** a list of topics for tonight's meeting.
2. The **preparation** of this delicious turkey dinner was easy.
3. It was a serious fire, but **miraculously** no one was injured.
4. It seemed like a **miracle** that the hurricane did so little damage.
5. A visit to the palace impressed Anna with the **majesty** of the prince.
6. At sunset, the snowcapped mountains presented a **majestic** setting.
7. Do you know the **geographic** region of the Windward Islands?
8. The teacher pointed to a globe as we discussed **geography**.
9. The police asked witnesses to **describe** what they had seen.
10. From his **description** of Tokyo, we can see it's a fascinating city.
11. During the **ritual** dance, men and women chanted words of praise.
12. Prayer is a religious practice, or **rite**, that is part of a ceremony.
13. Using **triangulation**, we measured the distance between the objects.
14. The three buildings outside the park form a **triangle**.
15. Did you **recognize** Lauretta from the picture you'd seen?
16. Your helpful contribution to the school deserves **recognition**.
17. Before you begin work, carefully **analyze** the steps to be taken.
18. An **analysis** of the blood indicated that the patient was cured.
19. What is the lesson to be learned from this **fable**?
20. Smiling and happy, the twins told us about their **fabulous** trip.

PLAN IV

● Iditarod	Ptarmigan
Nome	caribou
Anchorage	parka
Aleutian Islands	blizzard
Alaska	icebound
Arctic	snowshoes
Bering Sea	headlamp
Yukon River	towline
Juneau	mukluks
moose	igloo

PLAN IV

1. The dogs were ready to begin the **Iditarod** Trail Sled Dog Race.
2. Gold was discovered in **Nome** in the early twentieth century.
3. A tremendous earthquake severely damaged **Anchorage** in 1964.
4. The **Aleutian Islands** form a long, thin chain in the ocean.
5. In 1959, **Alaska** became the 49th state admitted to the Union.
6. Surrounding the North Pole is a region called the **Arctic**.
7. The **Bering Sea** is located north of the Pacific Ocean.
8. During the winter the **Yukon River** is clogged with ice.
9. The state government has offices in the capital city, **Juneau.**
10. Using its antlers, the male **moose** is able to defend itself.
11. The town of **Ptarmigan** was named for a bird that lives in cold climates.
12. With its front hooves, the **caribou** scrapes the snow in search of food.
13. Bundle up in this **parka** to keep yourself warm.
14. Heavy snow fell for three days during last winter's **blizzard**.
15. We couldn't sail to the harbor because it was **icebound**.
16. **Snowshoes** will help you walk more easily in the deep snow.
17. The **headlamp** was turned on as the train approached the tunnel.
18. Pulling the **towline**, the sailors brought the boat to shore.
19. Wearing **mukluks** is a good way to keep your feet warm.
20. The **igloo** is the traditional home of the Eskimo people.

nylon	trampoline
tarmac	escalator
dynamite	thermos
aspirin	tabloid
cellophane	aluminum
linoleum	windbreaker
minibike	spoof
yo-yo	blurb
zippered	boondoggle
kerosene	scrooge

1. My new lightweight backpack is made of **nylon**.
2. His flight landed smoothly on the airport **tarmac**.
3. Officials used **dynamite** to destroy the old building.
4. Take some **aspirin** if you have a headache.
5. The child tore the shiny **cellophane** wrap from the new toy.
6. In our new house we wanted **linoleum** on the kitchen floor.
7. Candice rode her **minibike** to visit her best friend.
8. I taught my younger brother how to play with a **yo-yo**.
9. The **zippered** pouch is a handy place to keep small items.
10. We used **kerosene** to start the campfire.
11. Have you tried jumping on the **trampoline** at the gym?
12. The store has an **escalator** from the first floor to the second.
13. The **thermos** will keep the soup hot until lunchtime.
14. Many newspaper readers prefer the smaller **tabloid**.
15. Portable furniture, such as beach chairs, is often made of **aluminum**.
16. In cool weather I wear jeans and a **windbreaker** to go hiking.
17. We laughed at the **spoof** of some of our favorite actors.
18. The **blurb** on the book jacket called the story an exciting mystery.
19. The project was more of a **boondoggle** than useful work.
20. I'm not a **scrooge**, but I do like to save my pennies.

technical	geographic
unique	triangulation
accident	towline
scheme	blizzard
guideline	Anchorage
equally	Arctic
definitely	Nome
probably	nylon
coastal	dynamite
merciful	aluminum
prepare	windbreaker
miraculously	kerosene
majestic	

1. This computer book is highly **technical**.
2. Carlos's visit to the Grand Canyon was a **unique** experience.
3. He wasn't seriously hurt in the automobile **accident**.
4. Will this **scheme** for building a model airplane really work?
5. The **guideline** gives us helpful information.
6. The rules apply **equally** to both teams in the game.
7. He **definitely** promised to finish the work today.
8. Jan will **probably** visit us today, but his plans are not final.
9. The boat neared the island's **coastal** waters.
10. The lawyer begged the judge to be **merciful** to the prisoner.
11. We should **prepare** a list of topics for tonight's meeting.
12. It was a serious fire, but **miraculously** no one was injured.
13. At sunset, the snowcapped mountains presented a **majestic** setting.
14. Do you know the **geographic** region of the Windward Islands?
15. Using **triangulation**, we measured the distance between the objects.
16. Pulling the **towline**, the sailors brought the boat to shore.
17. Heavy snow fell for three days during last winter's **blizzard**.
18. A tremendous earthquake severely damaged **Anchorage** in 1964.
19. Surrounding the North Pole is a region called the **Arctic**.
20. Gold was discovered in **Nome** in the early twentieth century.
21. My new lightweight backpack is made of **nylon**.
22. Officials used **dynamite** to destroy the old building.
23. Portable furniture, such as beach chairs, is often made of **aluminum**.
24. In cool weather I wear jeans and a **windbreaker** to go hiking.
25. We used **kerosene** to start the campfire.

PLAN I

beggar	manager
flavor	senator
collar	visitor
peddler	sculptor
liar	mirror
scholar	actual
cellar	factual
pillar	Capitol
sponsor	capital
editor	customers

PLAN I

1. The **beggar** stood huddled in a doorway, holding out an empty cup.
2. Which **flavor** of ice cream do you prefer—vanilla or chocolate?
3. Jed turned up his coat **collar** against the biting wind.
4. The **peddler** opened his pack and began to show his wares.
5. If the witness identified my client, then she is a **liar**.
6. The Japanese history **scholar** flew to Tokyo to continue her studies.
7. Mrs. Lee went down to the **cellar** to check on the water heater.
8. The central **pillar** supporting the hall has weakened.
9. Duffy's Hardware is the **sponsor** of the local softball team.
10. The **editor** used a red pencil to make changes in the manuscript.
11. The diner complained to the **manager** that his food was cold.
12. The two candidates for state **senator** will hold a debate.
13. Dr. Lopez is a **visitor** to our country from Mexico.
14. The **sculptor** has turned the block of marble into a delicate statue.
15. The actor checked his costume in the full-length **mirror**.
16. The movie seemed to last forever, but its **actual** length was two hours.
17. The researcher spent hours in the library to prepare a **factual** report.
18. We visited the **Capitol** building in Washington, D.C.
19. Begin the greeting and closing of a letter with a **capital** letter.
20. The **customers** lined up early on the day of the big sale.

PLAN II

mileage	broken
marriage	slacken
percentage	lengthen
shortage	lessen
postage	dampen
censorship	regulation
fellowship	location
partnership	indication
ownership	irritation
relationship	stockholders

PLAN II

1. This new sports car doesn't get good gas **mileage**.
2. The Schillers just celebrated the tenth anniversary of their **marriage**.
3. What **percentage** of teenagers have tried cigarettes this year?
4. The **shortage** of food in the East caused many people to head west.
5. That heavy letter will require extra **postage**.
6. The library sponsored a meeting to discuss the **censorship** of books.
7. Ken enjoyed the **fellowship** of his old classmates at their fifth reunion.
8. The three lawyers decided to form a **partnership**.
9. Kaybee Realty has taken over **ownership** of that apartment building.
10. My **relationship** with my sister has improved since we have separate rooms.
11. That valuable vase was **broken** when we moved.
12. The police will not **slacken** their efforts to find the jewel thief.
13. The days **lengthen** as summer approaches.
14. The hours of daylight **lessen** as winter draws near.
15. Nothing could **dampen** his spirits on the day of his birthday party.
16. Beth studied each **regulation** before taking her driving test.
17. Next week Town Records will move to a new **location**.
18. The teacher's frown was an **indication** that he was getting annoyed.
19. The **irritation** to my eyes was caused by the smoke in the room.
20. The **stockholders** voted for a new board of directors for the company.

design	nation
designate	national
electric	pirate
electricity	piracy
medical	agent
medicine	agency
critic	promote
criticize	promotion
native	magic
nativity	magician

1. Eduardo will **design** the cover of the class magazine.
2. Did the teacher **designate** Martha class monitor in her absence?
3. Thomas Edison invented the **electric** light.
4. All **electricity** to the city was cut off during the power failure.
5. After college, she plans to attend **medical** school.
6. The doctor prescribed **medicine** for the child's sore throat.
7. Alvin's mother is the movie **critic** for the local newspaper.
8. Please don't **criticize** my speech until I've finished writing it.
9. Kangaroos are **native** to Australia.
10. The teacher told us that **nativity** is another word for birth.
11. Our **nation** tries to provide liberty and justice for all.
12. The seat of our **national** government is in Washington, D.C.
13. Blackbeard was a famous **pirate** who attacked ships in the early 1700s.
14. Today **piracy** usually refers to using copyrighted or trademarked material.
15. The travel **agent** planned a trip to Italy for the Martini family.
16. Cora works in the new travel **agency** on Union Boulevard.
17. We made several posters to **promote** our class bake sale.
18. Jamal's **promotion** to chief mechanic made his family proud.
19. My brother enjoys doing **magic** tricks.
20. The **magician** pulled a bouquet of flowers from his hat.

row	lead
sow	buffet
invalid	console
wound	shower
refuse	conduct
bowed	contract
tear	present
bass	entrance
dove	desert
sewers	research

1. We must **row** faster if we want to catch the other boat.
2. Dottie has raised her prize **sow** since it was a piglet.
3. That agreement is **invalid** because it was not signed by both parties.
4. Mom **wound** up the clock, and it began to tick.
5. If you **refuse** to clean your room, Dad may become angry.
6. The actors **bowed** as the audience applauded.
7. Grandma will mend the **tear** in your jacket.
8. Uncle Ben caught two **bass** and a trout in the lake.
9. Do you know how the **dove** became the symbol of peace?
10. Because of the heavy rain, many **sewers** in town are overflowing.
11. Yolanda was given the **lead** in the class play.
12. The **buffet** table held salads, meats, breads, fruits, and desserts.
13. I tried to **console** my little brother when his pet fish died.
14. The **shower** ended suddenly, and the sun came out.
15. The leader raised his baton and began to **conduct** the band.
16. The **contract** was finally signed by both parties.
17. I will bring her birthday **present** to the party Saturday.
18. The main **entrance** to the library is on Worth Street.
19. Camels can store water and thus are good **desert** animals.
20. Carlos did **research** at the library before starting to write his report.

flurry	flush
smog	smash
splatter	slosh
brunch	sprig
squiggle	telecast
motel	co-op
twirl	broasted
splotch	movie
bionic	dumbfound
glimmer	bike

PLAN V

1. There was a **flurry** of activity in the house before the guests arrived.
2. The lack of wind caused **smog** around the city.
3. Move the brush carefully so you don't **splatter** the paint.
4. Since it was late morning, we decided to have **brunch** instead of breakfast.
5. Is that **squiggle** supposed to be an *i* or an *e*?
6. On our way home from Grandma's, we spent the night in a **motel**.
7. That drum major can really **twirl** a baton.
8. The spilled juice formed an orange **splotch** on the tablecloth.
9. The worker used a **bionic** hand to grasp the superhot machine part.
10. We could see a **glimmer** of light at the end of the tunnel.
11. The compliment caused a **flush** of pleasure to spread across her cheeks.
12. You will **smash** the glass with that hammer if you aren't careful.
13. My little sister likes to **slosh** through the puddles in her new boots.
14. The florist put a **sprig** of holly in the winter bouquet.
15. The nominating speech was **telecast** from the convention floor.
16. My aunt and uncle hope to buy a **co-op** apartment in that new building.
17. The **broasted** chicken was very tasty.
18. Have you seen the new animated **movie** playing in town?
19. The play's elaborate sets will **dumbfound** the audience.
20. Lorna's new mountain **bike** is a beauty.

PLAN VI

flavor	promote
peddler	promotion
sponsor	refuse
visitor	tear
capital	lead
mileage	conduct
marriage	desert
relationship	splatter
broken	squiggle
regulation	bionic
designate	glimmer
medical	telecast
medicine	

PLAN VI

1. Which **flavor** of ice cream do you prefer—vanilla or chocolate?
2. The **peddler** opened his pack and began to show his wares.
3. Duffy's Hardware is the **sponsor** of the local softball team.
4. Dr. Lopez is a **visitor** to our country from Mexico.
5. Begin the greeting and closing of a letter with a **capital** letter.
6. This new sports car doesn't get good gas **mileage**.
7. The Schillers just celebrated the tenth anniversary of their **marriage**.
8. My **relationship** with my sister has improved since we have separate rooms.
9. That valuable vase was **broken** when we moved.
10. Beth studied each **regulation** before taking her driving test.
11. Did the teacher **designate** Martha class monitor in her absence?
12. After college, she plans to attend **medical** school.
13. The doctor prescribed **medicine** for the child's sore throat.
14. We made several posters to **promote** our class bake sale.
15. Jamal's **promotion** to chief mechanic made his family proud.
16. If you **refuse** to clean your room, Dad may become angry.
17. Grandma will mend the **tear** in your jacket.
18. Yolanda was given the **lead** in the class play.
19. The leader raised his baton and began to **conduct** the band.
20. Camels can store water and thus are good **desert** animals.
21. Move the brush carefully so you don't **splatter** the paint.
22. Is that **squiggle** supposed to be an *i* or an *e*?
23. The worker used a **bionic** hand to grasp the superhot machine part.
24. We could see a **glimmer** of light at the end of the tunnel.
25. The nominating speech was **telecast** from the convention floor.

exchanging	ancient
establish	appreciate
ferocious	crucial
vision	concerto
decision	exhaustion
snatching	challenge
conditions	sugar
measure	erosion
casual	equation
century	chariot

1. I am **exchanging** this autobiography for a book of short stories.
2. We are going to **establish** a new theater that will present plays for children.
3. The **ferocious** dog snarled and bared its teeth.
4. I wear glasses because my **vision** is poor without them.
5. My **decision** is to take the baby-sitting job on Thursday evening.
6. That dog keeps **snatching** my newspaper and running away with it.
7. If the weather **conditions** are good, we will have a picnic on Sunday.
8. Please **measure** the length and the width of this room.
9. I wore **casual** clothes—jeans and a sweater—to the picnic.
10. A **century** ago, in the late 1800s, people regularly used horses for transportation.
11. These **ancient** pottery bowls must be over a thousand years old.
12. We all **appreciate** the great work that you do every day.
13. Your vote is **crucial** to the election of our candidate.
14. The orchestra played my favorite **concerto** last night.
15. We worked to **exhaustion** cleaning up the park.
16. The team accepted our **challenge** to play another baseball game.
17. Too much **sugar** in the lemonade makes it taste too sweet.
18. Wind and rain caused severe **erosion** of the hillside behind my house.
19. With my knowledge of math, I can easily solve this **equation**.
20. The painting of ancient Rome showed a team of horses pulling a **chariot**.

suppressed	deputy
depression	captured
express	capable
impression	captive
compress	capacity
dispute	capsule
compute	contest
computation	testify
repute	detest
reputation	protest

1. Because the news was **suppressed,** no one found out what happened until this morning.
2. The **depression** in the rock always fills with water when it rains.
3. **Express** your thoughts clearly, or no one will understand what you mean.
4. The new girls' basketball coach made a good **impression** on the players.
5. **Compress** the cans so they take up less space.
6. We had a **dispute** over who would do the dishes.
7. Use your calculator to **compute** the cost of this bicycle.
8. My **computation** shows how many children visit the zoo every year.
9. A person of good **repute** is kind and thoughtful.
10. Her **reputation** as an artist is excellent.
11. The sheriff hired a **deputy** to help her.
12. I **captured** a spider, and then let it loose outside.
13. She is **capable** of playing jump rope very skillfully.
14. The **captive** tiger broke out of its cage.
15. This container has a **capacity** of two quarts.
16. We buried a time **capsule** under the tree in our backyard.
17. Five good spellers from my class entered the spelling **contest**.
18. Three witnesses to the crime will **testify** in court.
19. Although some people **detest** snakes, I really like them.
20. We **protest** the replacement of our city park with a parking lot.

nature	attractive
natural	attract
naturalist	unattractive
naturalistic	distract
unnatural	distraction
envision	tractor
visual	supposed
visibility	juxtaposes
invisible	proposal
invisibility	deposit

1. Of all the living things in **nature**, I like animals the best.
2. That lake is **natural** and has been there for thousands of years.
3. The **naturalist** gave a talk about the plants and animals in the park.
4. The characters in that **naturalistic** play talked like real people.
5. In my hometown, it is **unnatural** for snow to fall in July.
6. I **envision** spending next summer hiking in the mountains.
7. The new movie about space has fantastic **visual** effects.
8. **Visibility** during the storm was so poor that I couldn't see the car.
9. Most gases, including oxygen, are **invisible**.
10. The **invisibility** of air makes it impossible to see.
11. My sister wore an **attractive** dress to the party.
12. The food at the picnic will **attract** many bugs.
13. Rudeness is an **unattractive** quality in children and adults.
14. Noise in the classroom will **distract** students who are studying.
15. The television was a **distraction** when I was trying to read.
16. With the **tractor**, we pulled a load of hay to the barn.
17. I **supposed** that everyone liked beets, but I was wrong.
18. The art critic **juxtaposes** the paintings to see how they are alike.
19. The **proposal** asks that all students in our school have a computer.
20. You can **deposit** your paycheck in the bank.

fangs	apron
orange	quiz
bonfire	galaxy
neighbor	tote
muscle	alarm
monster	geranium
silhouetted	debris
cyclone	planet
asteroid	tentacles
umpire	salary

1. When the snake opened its mouth, I saw its long, sharp **fangs**.
2. This is the sweetest **orange** I have ever tasted.
3. We built a **bonfire** and burned stacks of old newspapers all at once.
4. My **neighbor** who lives across the street really likes animals.
5. This **muscle** in my leg is sore from running.
6. The **monster** in the movie was ugly and scary-looking.
7. The large ship was **silhouetted** against the evening sky.
8. That **cyclone** was one of the worst storms of the year.
9. The camera on the spaceship took a photograph of a passing **asteroid**.
10. Jane is the fairest **umpire** in our baseball league.
11. Before I began to prepare dinner, I put on my **apron**.
12. In math class, we had a surprise **quiz** on long division.
13. All the planets and stars in our **galaxy** are known as the Milky Way.
14. That is a heavy load to **tote** up the hill.
15. When the fire **alarm** sounded, everyone left the building.
16. I planted a **geranium** in the flower box by the kitchen door.
17. The ground was covered with **debris** from the ruined building.
18. Earth is the third **planet** from the sun.
19. The octopus wrapped two **tentacles** around a rock.
20. She earns an excellent **salary** as an actress.

PLAN V

stationary   farther
stationery   further
immigrate   principal
emigrate   principle
accept   proceed
except   precede
affect   collage
effects   college
envelop   forward
envelope   foreword

PLAN V

1. The **stationary** bench was nailed to the floor.
2. I wrote the thank-you note on my best **stationery**.
3. People who **immigrate** to the United States will make it their permanent home.
4. My friends decided to **emigrate** from Ireland to the United States.
5. Please **accept** this gift from all your friends.
6. Everyone **except** me has seen that movie about whales.
7. Lack of snow will definitely **affect** our plans to go skiing.
8. The **effects** of this flu are aching joints and a bad cough.
9. On cool nights, the fog will **envelop** the whole town.
10. I put my letter in a stamped and addressed **envelope** and mailed it.
11. She can kick a ball **farther** than I can.
12. We **further** reduced the weight of the box by removing several heavy books.
13. The **principal** of our school was once a sixth-grade teacher.
14. Being truthful is one **principle** my family always follows.
15. The train will **proceed** after the track is repaired.
16. At the class assembly, three songs will **precede** the humorous skit.
17. The artist made a **collage** of pictures and words from magazines.
18. After high school, many students plan to go on to **college**.
19. The baby took two steps **forward**.
20. In the **foreword** to this collection of poems, the editor explains his purpose.

PLAN VI

ferocious   distraction
vision   unnatural
ancient   silhouetted
erosion   galaxy
challenge   debris
reputation   cyclone
impression   tentacles
dispute   stationery
capable   except
testify   effects
juxtaposes   immigrate
proposal   principal
invisible

PLAN VI

1. The **ferocious** dog snarled and bared its teeth.
2. I wear glasses because my **vision** is poor without them.
3. These **ancient** pottery bowls must be over a thousand years old.
4. Wind and rain caused severe **erosion** of the hillside behind my house.
5. The team accepted our **challenge** to play another baseball game.
6. Her **reputation** as an artist is excellent.
7. The new girls' basketball coach made a good **impression** on the players.
8. We had a **dispute** over who would do the dishes.
9. She is **capable** of playing jump rope very skillfully.
10. Three witnesses to the crime will **testify** in court.
11. The art critic **juxtaposes** the paintings to see how they are alike.
12. The **proposal** asks that all students in our school have a computer.
13. Most gases, including oxygen, are **invisible**.
14. The television was a **distraction** when I was trying to read.
15. In my hometown, it is **unnatural** for snow to fall in July.
16. The large ship was **silhouetted** against the evening sky.
17. All the planets and stars in our **galaxy** are known as the Milky Way.
18. The ground was covered with **debris** from the ruined building.
19. That **cyclone** was one of the worst storms of the year.
20. The octopus wrapped two **tentacles** around a rock.
21. I wrote the thank-you note on my best **stationery**.
22. Everyone **except** me has seen that movie about whales.
23. The **effects** of this flu are aching joints and a bad cough.
24. People who **immigrate** to the United States will make it their permanent home.
25. The **principal** of our school was once a sixth-grade teacher.

gorgeous   endorse

compartments   platform

starboard   corporation

startled   radar

partial   assortment

enormous   parcel

organize   dormitory

hearth   harvest

cornstarch   department

boulevard   starvation

PLAN I

1. The model on the magazine cover was wearing a **gorgeous** gown.
2. This handy travel bag has several **compartments** for organizing items.
3. Port means the left side of a ship, and **starboard** means the right.
4. The car's headlights **startled** the deer.
5. Dwayne received only **partial** credit until he completed the assignment.
6. They are so rich that they live in an **enormous** mansion.
7. **Organize** your desk by putting your papers in order.
8. The children sat close to the **hearth** to enjoy the fire's warmth.
9. Add **cornstarch** to the gravy to thicken it.
10. Colorful spring flowers lined both sides of the **boulevard.**
11. You must **endorse** the check before you can cash it.
12. The speaker mounted the **platform** and took the microphone.
13. Janice's mother works for a large **corporation** in the city.
14. The air traffic controller monitored the planes on his **radar** screen.
15. This sweater in the catalog comes in an **assortment** of colors.
16. Please take this **parcel** to the post office and mail it.
17. The Alonzos helped their daughter move into her college **dormitory**.
18. Thanks to plentiful rain, this year's **harvest** will be a good one.
19. In which **department** of the college does your father teach?
20. Let's have lunch before I die of **starvation**!

PLAN II

ejected   aggravate

project   atmosphere

dejected   stratosphere

objection   hemisphere

adjective   spherical

subject   aspire

gravitational   conspire

grave   expire

gravity   inspire

gravitate   perspire

PLAN II

1. The videocassette recorder automatically **ejected** the videocassette.
2. Our social studies **project** is a diorama of the Boston Tea Party.
3. The puppy looked so sad and **dejected**, I had to take her home.
4. I have no **objection** to having our class party next Thursday.
5. An **adjective** describes a noun.
6. The **subject** of my report is animal life in the Arctic.
7. **Gravitational** force pulls everything toward the center of the earth.
8. Our teacher's face looked very **grave** when she passed back our tests.
9. She said we did not understand the **gravity** of the situation.
10. Since I love the color red, I **gravitate** toward roses and other red flowers.
11. Loud music played at night is just one of the things that **aggravate** me.
12. After the fire drill, the **atmosphere** in the room was very tense.
13. The **stratosphere** is the upper region of the earth's atmosphere.
14. Australia is in the southern **hemisphere**.
15. The earth is **spherical**.
16. Tim and Paula **aspire** to be in the movies someday.
17. Rachel and Ruth **conspire** to make a surprise party for Deisha.
18. The girls watched the flames in their campfire slowly **expire**.
19. Great books always **inspire** me to become a writer.
20. Exercise makes most people **perspire**.

conversation	irreversible
converse	irreversibility
verse	admit
convert	submit
conversion	transmit
universe	dismiss
universal	commit
university	commission
reverse	correspond
reversible	correspondent

1. We had a great **conversation** about our favorite books.
2. Jim and Paul **converse** on the phone for two hours every night.
3. I memorized the first **verse** of my favorite poem.
4. Stella didn't believe in recycling, but the class managed to **convert** her.
5. After her **conversion**, Stella worked at the recycling office.
6. Have you ever wondered how big the **universe** is?
7. The love of ice cream is almost **universal**.
8. Carmen hopes to go to the same **university** her mother attended.
9. The answers to the riddles are on the **reverse** side of the paper.
10. Ellen bought a **reversible** raincoat that was a different color on each side.
11. After next week, your decision not to be in the play will be **irreversible**.
12. Tilly felt bad about the **irreversibility** of her decision.
13. No one would **admit** to erasing the problem from the board.
14. The teacher asked us to **submit** our final papers on Friday.
15. The coaches **transmit** a daily message at 10 a.m.
16. The gym teachers always **dismiss** us early so we can change.
17. The whole class could **commit** to tutoring one afternoon a week.
18. The **commission** on improving the library suggested changes in policy.
19. Greg and I still **correspond** by mail.
20. He writes longer letters and is generally a better **correspondent** than I am.

bagel	pajamas
clown	yam
chocolate	coffee
landscape	hammock
ketchup	kangaroo
spinach	tundra
bandit	gorilla
karate	jubilee
bamboo	outrage
ukulele	investigation

1. For breakfast I ate a whole-wheat **bagel** smeared with low-fat cream cheese.
2. The **clown** made everyone at the circus laugh.
3. The candy that I like the least is **chocolate.**
4. My brother painted a desert **landscape** with cactus and dry rolling hills.
5. My little sister pours **ketchup** on everything she eats.
6. Mom picked **spinach** from our garden and steamed it for dinner.
7. The **bandit** who stole my watch was later caught.
8. **Karate** is a method of self-defense that originated in Japan.
9. Much of the **bamboo** that grows in the tropics is made into furniture.
10. Jane played a Hawaiian song on her **ukulele**.
11. I wore my red, white, and blue **pajamas** to bed last night.
12. The **yam** is my favorite root vegetable.
13. **Coffee** was one of the beverage choices on the menu.
14. I hung a **hammock** between the two trees, and then took a nap in it.
15. While I was visiting Australia, I saw a wild **kangaroo** hopping across the road.
16. The land in Alaska known as the **tundra** is flat and treeless.
17. Did you know that the **gorilla**, the largest of all the apes, is native to equatorial Africa?
18. My school will celebrate its 75th **jubilee** next spring.
19. It's an **outrage** that so many people throw their litter in the street.
20. There will be an **investigation** into the disappearance of the muffins.

enchantment | journey

appeal | trek

panic | cruise

hysteria | voyage

intrude | horror

disturb | terror

messenger | dread

carrier | demand

necessary | command

vital | order

1. My **enchantment** with the ocean began on a visit to the seashore.
2. The movie lost its **appeal** after I saw it a third time.
3. He felt **panic** when he saw the fire engines stop in front of his house.
4. Karna was filled with **hysteria** when she smelled smoke.
5. Please don't **intrude** on the rehearsal of the class play.
6. Do not **disturb** the baby while she is napping, or she will start crying.
7. The **messenger** brought an important letter to the president.
8. The large white-and-green truck is a lumber **carrier**.
9. It's **necessary** to buy some snacks for my birthday party.
10. The weather bureau broadcast **vital** information on the hurricane.
11. Our **journey** took us across the Great Plains and ended in Oregon.
12. Our slow **trek** across the desert was filled with difficulty.
13. My sister is going on a sailboat **cruise** to several islands.
14. The spacecraft completed the long **voyage** to the moon.
15. **Horror** is not a pleasant emotion to feel.
16. I was filled with **terror** when I discovered that I was lost.
17. The sight of a spider causes **dread** in some people.
18. The miners **demand** safer working conditions.
19. I **command** you to stop making that noise right now!
20. The generals **order** their troops to march in good and bad weather.

enormous | correspondent

assortment | commit

endorse | landscape

gorgeous | chocolate

parcel | outrage

aggravate | ketchup

atmosphere | investigation

gravitational | enchantment

objection | panic

perspire | disturb

universal | hysteria

university | messenger

reversible

1. They are so rich that they live in an **enormous** mansion.
2. This sweater in the catalog comes in an **assortment** of colors.
3. You must **endorse** the check before you cash it.
4. The model on the magazine cover was wearing a **gorgeous** gown.
5. Please take this **parcel** to the post office and mail it.
6. Loud music played at night is just one of the things that **aggravate** me.
7. After the fire drill, the **atmosphere** in the room was very tense.
8. **Gravitational** force pulls everything toward the center of the earth.
9. I have no **objection** to having our class party next Thursday.
10. Exercise makes most people **perspire**.
11. The love of ice cream is almost **universal**.
12. Carmen hopes to go to the same **university** her mother attended.
13. Ellen bought a **reversible** raincoat that was a different color on each side.
14. He writes longer letters and is generally a better **correspondent** than I am.
15. The whole class could **commit** to tutoring one afternoon a week.
16. My brother painted a desert **landscape** with cactus and dry rolling hills.
17. The candy that I like the least is **chocolate**.
18. It's an **outrage** that so many people throw their litter in the street.
19. My little sister pours **ketchup** on everything she eats.
20. There will be an **investigation** into the disappearance of the muffins.
21. My **enchantment** with the ocean began on a visit to the seashore.
22. He felt **panic** when he saw the fire engines stop in front of his house.
23. Do not **disturb** the baby while she is napping, or she will start crying.
24. Karna was filled with **hysteria** when she smelled smoke.
25. The **messenger** brought an important letter to the president.

general	terrify
generate	terrific
accuse	popular
accusation	popularity
crime	original
criminal	origin
ridicule	courage
ridiculous	courageous
punctuation	real
punctual	reality

1. The **general** commanded a group of soldiers in the army.
2. Water power can be used to **generate** electricity.
3. Please don't **accuse** me of being untidy.
4. This **accusation** says that people left litter in the park after the picnic.
5. Did you know that littering on the highway is a **crime**?
6. In the story, the **criminal** was captured by the police.
7. When you **ridicule** your little brother, he feels bad and runs away.
8. That silly costume is the most **ridiculous** thing I have ever seen.
9. A question mark is the **punctuation** you use at the end of a question.
10. I promise that I will be **punctual** for our appointment.
11. Scary rides at amusement parks **terrify** me.
12. The party was lots of fun and we had a **terrific** time.
13. All of my friends have read this very **popular** book.
14. I am surprised by the **popularity** of this television show.
15. The **original** owner of this bicycle took good care of it.
16. We discussed the **origin** of baseball with the coach.
17. It takes **courage** to say what you believe.
18. The **courageous** firefighter rescued a dog from the burning building.
19. I will tell you my **real** reason for leaving the party early.
20. My dream of winning the race became a **reality**.

suggest	effort
occupied	sufficient
affairs	collaborate
account	appetite
appearance	irregular
assumed	immense
committee	assignment
commotion	annex
illegal	suppress
immature	attorneys

1. I **suggest** that you study hard for the social studies test.
2. Last year, this house was **occupied** by a family with three children.
3. Graduation is one of the year's most important **affairs**.
4. Tomorrow I will give an **account** of what I did during my vacation.
5. I was pleased by the **appearance** of several friends at my dance recital.
6. I **assumed** that the plane would arrive on time, but I was wrong.
7. I am on the **committee** that is organizing recycling in my school.
8. During the storm, a falling tree caused a **commotion** among my neighbors.
9. Did you know that it is **illegal** to park your car in a bus zone?
10. This **immature** pear is still hard and sour.
11. It took a lot of **effort** to build that house.
12. Our class raised **sufficient** money to buy a new computer.
13. Two of us will **collaborate** on creating a banner for our classroom.
14. My brother has a big **appetite** and always eats large meals.
15. Each side of this **irregular** box is a different length.
16. The pumpkin was so **immense** that I could barely lift it.
17. My **assignment** is to read 20 pages by Friday.
18. The school built a small **annex** to the library.
19. During the ceremony, please **suppress** any desire to laugh.
20. Two **attorneys** will defend their client during the trial.

democratic	gene
democracy	genetic
astronaut	autobiography
astronomy	automobile
microscope	automatic
telescope	autograph
diameter	paragraph
dialects	alphabet
metric	microphone
thermometer	kaleidoscope

1. The Bill of Rights is a **democratic** statement.
2. The government of the United States of America is a **democracy**.
3. The **astronaut** circled the earth in the space shuttle.
4. **Astronomy** is the scientific study of the sun, moon, planets, stars, comets, and galaxies.
5. Through a **microscope**, a shaft of hair looks enormous.
6. We looked at the moon through a **telescope.**
7. The **diameter** of the circle is three feet.
8. People who live in this region speak several different **dialects**.
9. The milliliter and liter are **metric** measurements of capacity.
10. We looked at the **thermometer** to find the outside temperature.
11. A **gene** is a tiny part of a plant or animal cell that determines a characteristic that is passed from parent to offspring.
12. The scientists study **genetic** material.
13. The author wrote an **autobiography** about her childhood.
14. He drove the **automobile** to the gas station.
15. **Automatic** washing machines take the work out of doing laundry.
16. We asked the sports star for his **autograph**.
17. I wrote a **paragraph** about one benefit of exercise.
18. The child wrote the **alphabet** from *a* to *z*.
19. Speak clearly into the **microphone** so everyone can understand you.
20. I looked into the **kaleidoscope** and saw a beautiful pattern.

PLAN IV

PLAN IV

legislature	archaeology
legislators	anthropologist
Congress	disease
convention	penicillin
citizen	veterinarian
community	continent
formula	climate
solve	environment
solution	population
diagram	suburb

1. The state **legislature** met in January to write and pass new laws.
2. The **legislators** passed three new laws last week.
3. **Congress** is made up of the United States Senate and the House of Representatives.
4. The delegates to the **convention** chose a presidential candidate.
5. As a **citizen** of the United States, I can vote when I turn eighteen.
6. The people in my **community** have a town picnic every summer.
7. There is no **formula** for writing an interesting short story.
8. I like to **solve** math problems.
9. There must be an easy **solution** to this problem.
10. I drew a **diagram** showing the different parts of a sailboat.
11. **Archaeology** is the study of people who lived in ancient times.
12. The **anthropologist** studies the customs of a Native American tribe.
13. The doctor found a cure for the **disease**.
14. **Penicillin** is an antibiotic used for treating infections.
15. The **veterinarian** treated small animals, such as cats and dogs.
16. North America is a **continent** between the Atlantic and Pacific oceans.
17. During the summer, the Mojave Desert's **climate** is hot and dry.
18. Laws now protect plants and animals in the **environment**.
19. The **population** of the city is now over a million people.
20. I live in a **suburb** just outside of Atlanta, Georgia.

tomorrow	perfect
money	school
stomach	soldier
bridge	debt
straight	doubt
aisle	surprise
ghost	rhyme
foreign	acre
island	scissors
limb	warden

PLAN V

1. I will study for the test **tomorrow**.
2. The **money** I saved will pay for a new baseball glove.
3. After I ate a large lunch, my **stomach** felt very full.
4. The **bridge** over the river was built of concrete and steel.
5. Using my ruler as a guide, I drew a **straight** line on the paper.
6. I walked down the **aisle** in the theater and quickly found my seat.
7. The **ghost** in the story turned out to be a bedsheet.
8. The explorer visited many **foreign** lands before she returned home.
9. I visited a tiny **island** just off the coast of Maine.
10. During the storm, a **limb** broke off the biggest tree in the park.
11. He is a **perfect** person for the job.
12. There are four classes of sixth graders in my **school**.
13. The **soldier** made many friends while he was in the army.
14. I avoid going into **debt** by paying all my bills immediately.
15. I **doubt** that he is telling the truth.
16. We will **surprise** Mom by doing the laundry.
17. The poet wrote a **rhyme** using the words *May* and *day*.
18. The old house sits on an **acre** of land.
19. I bought a pair of **scissors** for cutting paper.
20. The fire **warden** sent out the new guidelines for fire prevention.

PLAN VI

accusation	diameter
ridiculous	automatic
popularity	citizen
criminal	solution
courageous	environment
sufficient	disease
account	legislature
committee	warden
occupied	straight
immense	stomach
democratic	foreign
astronaut	acre
telescope	

PLAN VI

1. This **accusation** says that people left litter in the park after the picnic.
2. That silly costume is the most **ridiculous** thing I have ever seen.
3. I am surprised by the **popularity** of this television show.
4. In the story, the **criminal** was captured by the police.
5. The **courageous** firefighter rescued a dog from the burning building.
6. Our class raised **sufficient** money to buy a new computer.
7. Tomorrow I will give an **account** of what I did during my vacation.
8. I am on the **committee** that is organizing recycling in my school.
9. Last year, this house was **occupied** by a family with three children.
10. The pumpkin was so **immense** that I could barely lift it.
11. The Bill of Rights is a **democratic** statement.
12. The **astronaut** circled the earth in the space shuttle.
13. We looked at the moon through a **telescope**.
14. The **diameter** of the circle is three feet.
15. **Automatic** washing machines take the work out of doing laundry.
16. As a **citizen** of the United States, I can vote when I turn eighteen.
17. There must be an easy **solution** to this problem.
18. Laws now protect plants and animals in the **environment**.
19. The doctor found a cure for the **disease**.
20. The state **legislature** met in January to write and pass new laws.
21. The fire **warden** sent out the new guidelines for fire prevention.
22. Using my ruler as a guide, I drew a **straight** line on the paper.
23. After I ate a large lunch, my **stomach** felt very full.
24. The explorer visited many **foreign** lands before she returned home.
25. The old house sits on an **acre** of land.

Page 1 - Unusual Spellings of Vowel Sounds

1. Jan ate an **orange** while she read the **magazine**.
2. Al's antics were a **nuisance** at the **matinee** performance.
3. He stuck his **tongue** out when the **curtain** came down. Then he tried to squeeze into my seat—I felt like a **sardine**!
4. Pat sent **bouquets** of roses and baskets of **fruit** to his mother to celebrate her birthday.
5. The heavy **weight** of the big copying **machine** made her stagger. Then she lay down on the couch and stared at the **ceiling**.
6. "The **pursuit** of information is fine," Dad said. But he wasn't facing my homework and had enough **leisure** time to read his newspaper.
7. For more **knowledge** about a subject, I consult an encyclopedia.
8. When the movers delivered the **statue** to the museum, they asked for a **receipt**.
9. Because Teresa was sick, she had to **forfeit** the last race. But after training hard, she plans to **seize** the lead and win the next time.
10. After the **burial** of Ian's pet frog, we all had a good cry.

Page 2 - Synonyms

A.

1. deserted **desolate, lonely**
2. excuse **forgive, pardon**
3. fondness **affection, tenderness**
4. hasty **abrupt, rapid, hurried**
5. gloomy **murky, obscure, unclear**
6. high-priced **costly, expensive**

B.

7. **lonely, costly**
8. **hasty, murky, gloomy**
9. **deserted, hurried, high-priced**
10. **tenderness, fondness**

Page 3 - Word Building and Sound Changes

1. **compete, competition**
2. **compose, compositions**
3. **poetry, poetic**
4. **relate, relative**
5. **declare, declaration**
6. **improvise, improvisation**
7. **grammar, grammatical**
8. **apply, application**
9. **history, historical**
10. **prior, priority**

Page 4 - Spelling Patterns

1. **rattlesnake; undertake, cheesecake, snowflake, namesake**
2. **flashlight; foresight, spaceflight, all right**
3. **footstool; toadstool, car pool, whirlpool**
4. **windblown; disown, well-known, overgrown, overthrown**
5. **image; heritage**

PAGE 5 - TECHNICAL WORDS

A.

1. closeup, telephoto, tripod
2. transparency
3. photojournalist, darkroom
4. documentary, cinematography
5. videotape, camcorder

B.

6. lens
7. photocopy
8. camera
9. microfilm
10. portrait

11. snapshots
12. focus
13. candid
14. aperture
15. animation

PAGE 6 - SPELLING REVIEW

Two-syllable words: **bouquets, nuisance, knowledge, receipt, obscure, abrupt, windblown, image, well-known, car pool, all right, portrait**

Three-syllable words: **magazine, desolate, expensive, affection, improvise, poetry**

Four-syllable words: **competition, application, historical, documentary** (or 5), **videotape, animation**

Five-syllable words: **documentary** (or 4), **photojournalist**

PAGE 7 - CONSONANTS /K/ AND /G/

A. gu:

1. fatigue
2. league
3. guideline
4. disguise
5. guardian
6. guarantee

ch:

7. technical
8. scheme
9. character

B.

10. unique
11. access
12. accordion
13. schedule
14. antique
15. cocoon
16. kingdoms
17. technique
18. accuse
19. occupy
20. accident

PAGE 8 - ADDING SUFFIXES

A.

Chart 1: **emotion** + al = **emotional**; **coast** + al = **coastal**; **ornament** + al = **ornamental**; **mercy** + ful = **merciful**; **mercy** + less = **merciless**; **harm** + ful = **harmful**; **harm** + less = **harmless**; **faith** + ful = **faithful**

Chart 2: **equal** + ly = **equally**; **definite** + ly = **definitely**; **probable** + ly = **probably**

- -

B. **mercy** changes *y* to *i*; **probable** drops the *e*

PAGE 9 - WORD BUILDING AND SOUND CHANGES

A.

1. (di skrīb´) **describe**
2. (jē og´ rə fē) **geography**
3. (mə jes´ tik) **majestic**
4. (mir´ ə kəl) **miracle**
5. (pri pâr´) **prepare**
6. (rek´ əg nīz) **recognize**
7. (di skrip´ shən) **description**
8. (jē ə graf´ ik) **geographic**
9. (maj´ ə stē) **majesty**
10. (mi rak´ yə ləs) **miraculous**
11. (prep ə rā´ shən) **preparation**
12. (rek əg nish´ ən) **recognition**

- -

B.

13. **fable; fabulous**
14. **triangle; triangulation**
15. **rite; ritual**
16. **analyze; analysis**

PAGE 10 - GEOGRAPHIC WORDS

A.

1. Alaska
2. Iditarod, Nome, Anchorage, Juneau, Ptarmigan
3. Bering Sea, Yukon River
4. Aleutian Islands
5. moose, caribou
6. parka, snowshoes, mukluks

B.

7. blizzards
8. icebound
9. Arctic
10. towline
11. igloo
12. headlamp

PAGE 11 - INVENTED WORDS

A.

1. trampoline, yo-yo, minibike, spoof
2. scrooge, boondoggle
3. linoleum, aluminum, nylon

B.

4. windbreaker, zippered, tarmac
5. thermos, cellophane
6. tabloid, Dynamite
7. kerosene
8. aspirin, escalator
9. blurb

PAGE 12 - SPELLING REVIEW

A.

1. accident, aluminum, Anchorage, Arctic
2. Nome, nylon, prepare, probably
3. technical, towline, triangulation, unique
4. merciful, miraculously
5. definitely, dynamite
6. geographic, guideline

B.

blizzard, windbreaker, coastal, majestic, kerosene, equally, scheme

PAGE 13 - THE SCHWA SOUND

1. peddler
2. sculptor
3. scholar
4. beggar

5. visitor
6. sponsor
7. liar
8. manager

9. senator
10. editor
11. customers

Sentences should use the words: **flavor, collar, cellar, pillar, mirror, Capitol,** and **capital** (nouns); **actual, factual** (adjectives).

PAGE 14 - SUFFIXES: *-age, -ship, -en, -tion, -er*

Words that are complete without their suffixes: **mileage, percentage, shortage, postage, censorship, fellowship, partnership, ownership, relationship, slacken, lengthen, lessen, dampen, stockholders**

Words that are incomplete without their suffixes: **marriage, regulation, location, indication, irritation, broken**

Word that is neither a noun nor a verb: **broken** (*adjective*)

PAGE 15 - STRESS SHIFT

Base word: **de<u>sign</u>, e<u>lec</u>tric, <u>med</u>ical, <u>crit</u>ic, <u>nat</u>ive, <u>na</u>tion, <u>pir</u>ate, <u>a</u>gent, pro<u>mote</u>, magic**

Base word + suffix: **<u>des</u>ignate, elec<u>tric</u>ity, <u>med</u>icine, <u>crit</u>icize, na<u>tiv</u>ity, <u>na</u>tional, <u>pir</u>acy, <u>a</u>gency, pro<u>mo</u>tion, ma<u>gic</u>ian**

PAGE 16 - HOMOGRAPHS

Nouns: **row, sow, invalid, wound, refuse, tear, bass, dove, sewers, lead, buffet, console, shower, conduct, contract, present, entrance, desert, research**

Verbs: **row, sow, wound, refuse, bowed, tear, dove, lead, buffet, console, shower, conduct, contract, present, entrance, desert, research**

Adjectives: **invalid, bowed, bass, present**

PAGE 17 - BLENDED AND SHORTENED WORDS

Blended words: **glimmer, smog, telecast, broasted, flurry, splatter, bionic, dumbfound, brunch, twirl, motel, squiggle, splotch, sprig, flush, slosh, smash**

Shortened words: **co-op, bike, movie**

PAGE 18 - SPELLING REVIEW

1-syllable words: **tear, lead**

2-syllable words: **fla/vor, ped/dler, spon/sor, mile/age, mar/riage, bro/ken, pro/mote, re/fuse, con/duct, de/sert, splat/ter, squig/gle, glim/mer**

3-syllable words: **vis/i/tor, cap/i/tal, des/ig/nate, med/i/cal, med/i/cine, pro/mo/tion, bi/on/ic, tel/e/cast**

4-syllable words: **re/la/tion/ship, reg/u/la/tion**

PAGE 19 - WORDS WITH /ch/, /sh/, /zh/

A.

Words with /sh/: establi(sh), condi(ti)ons, cru(ci)al, fero(ci)ous, appre(ci)ate, (s)ugar

- -

B.

Words with /zh/: vi(si)on, mea(s)ure, ero(si)on, deci(si)on, ca(s)ual, equa(ti)on

- -

C.

Words with /ch/: ex(ch)anging, cen(t)ury, con(c)erto, (ch)ariot, snat(ch)ing, an(ci)ent, exhaus(ti)on, (ch)allenge

PAGE 20 - BASES: *press, put, cap, test*

1. **depression**
2. **express**
3. **suppressed**
4. **compress**
5. **impression**
6. **captive**
7. **captured**
8. **capacity**
9. **capsule**
10. **capable**

Words with *test*: **contest, testify, detest, protest**

Words with *put*: **dispute, compute, computation, repute, reputation, deputy**

PAGE 21 - BASES AND ROOTS: *nat, vis, tract, pos*

A.

Nouns: **tractor, distraction**

Adjectives: **attractive, unattractive**

Verbs: **attract, distract**

- -

B.

1. **naturalist:** **nature, natural, naturalistic, unnatural**

2. **envision:** **visibility, invisible, invisibility, visual**

3. **deposit:** **juxtaposes, proposal, suppose**

PAGE 22- WORD HISTORIES

1. orange
2. apron
3. monster
4. geranium
5. planet
6. umpire
7. galaxy
8. muscle
9. quiz
10. tote
11. bonfire
12. tentacles
13. salary
14. alarm
15. fangs
16. neighbor
17. silhouetted
18. asteroids
19. debris
20. cyclone

PAGE 23 - WORD PAIRS

A.

1. college
2. forward
3. stationary
4. principle
5. affects
6. proceed
7. immigrate
8. precede
9. foreword
10. stationery
11. principal
12. effects
13. emigrate
14. collage

B.

15. accept
16. Further
17. envelop
18. except
19. envelope
20. farther

PAGE 24 - SPELLING REVIEW

Nouns: **vision, erosion, challenge, reputation, impression, dispute, proposal, distraction, debris, galaxy, cyclone, tentacles, stationery, effects, principal**

Verbs: **challenge, dispute, testify, juxtaposes, silhouetted, except, effects, immigrate**

Adjectives: **ferocious, ancient, capable, invisible, unnatural, principal**

Preposition: **except**

PAGE 25 - WORDS WITH /är/ AND /ôr/

A.

1. he<u>ar</u>th
2. boule<u>var</u>d
3. rad<u>ar</u>
4. h<u>ar</u>vest
5. st<u>ar</u>tled
6. st<u>ar</u>vation
7. comp<u>ar</u>tments
8. dep<u>ar</u>tment
9. p<u>ar</u>tial
10. cornst<u>ar</u>ch
11. p<u>ar</u>cel
12. st<u>ar</u>board
13. en<u>or</u>mous
14. <u>or</u>ganize
15. c<u>or</u>nstarch
16. end<u>or</u>se
17. platf<u>or</u>m
18. c<u>or</u>poration
19. ass<u>or</u>tment
20. d<u>or</u>mitory
21. g<u>or</u>geous

B.

22. cornstarch
23. dormitory
24. hearth

PAGE 26 - ROOTS: *JECT, GRAV, SPHER, SPIR*

A.

1. perspire
2. spherical
3. grave
4. aspire
5. aggravate
6. hemisphere
7. dejected
8. project
9. conspire
10. adjective
11. ejected
12. gravity
13. gravitate
14. expire

B.

15. stratosphere
16. inspire
17. atmosphere
18. subject
19. gravitational
20. objection

PAGE 27 - ROOTS: *VERT/VERS, MIT/MISS, SPOND*

Noun: conversation, converse, conversion, convert, correspondent, commission, irreversibility, reverse, universe, university, verse

Verb: admit, commission, commit, converse, convert, correspond, dismiss, reverse, submit, transmit

Adjective: irreversible, reverse, reversible, universal

PAGE 28 - WORDS FROM LANGUAGES OTHER THAN ENGLISH

A.

1. spinach
2. clown
3. kangaroo
4. landscape

5. bagel
6. coffee
7. chocolate

8. pajamas
9. bamboo
10. hammock

B.

11. investigation
12. ukulele
13. gorilla
14. tundra

15. bandit
16. outrage
17. karate

18. jubilee
19. ketchup
20. yam

PAGE 29 - WORDS WITH RELATED MEANINGS

1. panic, horror, terror, dread
2. panic; hysteria
3. journey, trek, cruise, voyage
4. demand, command, order; command, order

5. intrude, disturb; intrude
6. necessary, vital; vital
7. enchantment, appeal; enchantment
8. messenger, carrier

PAGE 30 - SPELLING REVIEW

A.

1. disturb
2. commit
3. endorse
4. atmosphere

5. parcel
6. objection
7. assortment
8. enormous

9. university
10. gorgeous
11. universal
12. correspondent

B.

13. chocolate
14. messenger
15. aggravate
16. panic
17. ketchup

18. outrage
19. hysteria
20. enchantment
21. gravitational

22. landscape
23. reversible
24. investigation
25. perspire

PAGE 31 - UNSTRESSED SYLLABLES

A.

1. pop´ u lar   pop u lar´ i ty
2. ri dic´ u lous   rid´ i cule
3. ac cuse´   ac cu sa´ tion
4. punc tu a´ tion   punc´ tu al
5. or´ i gin   o rig´ i nal
6. cou ra´ geous   cour´ age

B.

7. general, generate; terrify, terrific   3 syllables
8. crime, criminal; real, reality

PAGE 32 - DOUBLE CONSONANTS

1. committee, commotion, immature, immense
2. occupied, account
3. affairs, effort, sufficient
4. assumed, assignment, suppress
5. committee, attorneys
6. appearance, appetite, suppress
7. illegal, collaborate
8. suggest, irregular, annex

PAGE 33 - GREEK ROOTS AND COMBINING FORMS

A.

1. astronaut, astronomy
2. autobiography, automobile, automatic, autograph
3. metric, thermometer, diameter
4. microscope, telescope, kaleidoscope
5. democrat, democracy

B.

6. gene
7. dialects
8. genetic
9. alphabet
10. microphone
11. paragraph

PAGE 34 - SPELLING ACROSS THE CURRICULUM

1. veterinarian
2. Penicillin, disease; formula
3. Congress; legislators, legislature
4. archaeology; anthropologist
5. climate, continent, environment
6. community, citizen, convention
7. solve, diagram; solution
8. population, suburb

PAGE 35 - OLD SPELLINGS TO NEW

A.

1. straight
2. aisle
3. ghost
4. foreign
5. island
6. limb
7. debt
8. doubt
9. rhyme
10. scissors

B.

Across: **tomorrow, acre, surprise, soldier, school**

Down: **bridge, money, warden, stomach, perfect**

PAGE 36 - SPELLING REVIEW

a-c: **account, accusation, acre, astronaut, automatic, citizen, committee, courageous, criminal**
d-j: **democratic, diameter, disease, environment, foreign, immense**
k-z: **legislature, occupied, popularity, ridiculous, solution, stomach, straight, sufficient, telescope, warden**